OSCILLOSCOPES

OSCILLOSCOPES
Functional Operation and Measuring Examples

Rien van Erk

*Philips Test and Measuring Instruments,
Eindhoven, The Netherlands*

McGraw-Hill Book Company

*New York   St. Louis   San Francisco   Auckland   Bogotá
Düsseldorf   Johannesburg   London   Madrid   Mexico
Montreal   New Delhi   Panama   Paris
São Paulo   Singapore   Sydney   Tokyo   Toronto*

Library of Congress Cataloging in Publication Data

Erk, Rien van, date.
Oscilloscopes.

Includes index.
1. Cathode ray oscilloscope.   I. Title.
TK7878.7.E84   621.37'4   78-8966
ISBN 0-07-067050-1

234567890   KPKP   765432109

The McGraw-Hill editors for this book were Tyler G. Hicks and Joseph
Williams, the designer was Elliot Epstein, and the production
supervisor was Frank Bellantoni. It was set in Baskerville by
Progressive Typographers.

Printed and bound by The Kingsport Press.

To Adri

CONTENTS

PREFACE

Modern oscilloscopes are finding use not only in the traditional electrical and electronic measuring areas but also in a wider number of fields, including applications where purely mechanical methods were used before. Apart from developing facilities to make modern oscilloscopes simpler and more straightforward to use, much effort has gone into keeping these instruments up to date with technology—from exploiting the latest large-scale integrated (LSI) circuitry for extra reliability to providing facilities to match the latest high-speed circuit elements.

Making the best use of any facility requires an understanding of the basic elements and how to apply them successfully. With the oscilloscope becoming rapidly established as almost the standard test and measuring instrument, the need to understand and get the best results out of it becomes paramount.

This book not only attempts to help the specialist electrical engineer make the most of the oscilloscope but also provides a solid basic understanding for the nonspecialist, such as the mechanical engineer discovering the advantages of combining electrical measurements with mechanical methods. Students will also get a basic understanding of oscilloscope operation.

Many books and booklets have already been written on the subject of oscilloscopes, but most of these either describe the electronic-circuit building blocks or are a collection of experiments with mainly electronic phenomena. This book is designed to emphasize the use of the oscilloscope to allow the best use of its various facilities.

Starting with a discussion of the basic functions of an oscilloscope, and particularly the cathode-ray tube, the various extra facilities available for operator convenience are quickly introduced. Special designs are required for some applications—such as storage and sampling—and these are explained in more detail. Probes form an essential link between the oscilloscope and the device under test. Therefore, a separate chapter on these is fully justified. This chapter finishes the section of the book on the basics of oscilloscopes.

Basics are pointless in isolation, so measurement pitfalls are explained in order to give the reader guidance in minimizing measurement mistakes. And to wrap up the subject, a whole series of exercises are provided showing how the oscilloscope can be exploited to the limits of its capabilities to provide maximum accuracy and resolution. Of necessity, these are mainly electrical applications and sufficient detail is provided to make them easily repeatable in the classroom.

Understanding the specifications of oscilloscopes is important for anyone contemplating buying such an instrument and this subject is dealt with by detailed explanations of the specifications of a simple oscilloscope and a sophisticated oscilloscope in Chapter 7.

A further aid to the nonspecialist and specialist alike is a glossary of over 200 terms and the tables of SI electrical units.

ACKNOWLEDGMENTS

Many contributions are necessary to complete a book such as this one and much information has been taken from existing publications of the Philips' house. One such publication is Joop Aartsen's book "Zeroing in on ones and zeros," which was used as a basis for Chapter 2.

Very valuable were the discussions with, and the willing assistance, of my laboratory staff and in particular the contribution of Toon Kluytmans, who patiently executed all test setups for the measuring examples.

Last, but by no means least, special credit must be given to Frank Bregman, who conscientiously read the draft and gave many valuable suggestions for improvements, so that this book could be completed in its present form, and to Paul McCallum who carried out the final reading.

RIEN VAN ERK

OSCILLOSCOPES

BASIC OPERATION OF
THE OSCILLOSCOPE

1.1   WHY VISUALIZATION OF THE SIGNAL?

The specific characteristics of a signal can be measured by a variety of instruments. For example, a counter can measure a signal's frequency or its period, and an ac voltmeter can measure the rms value of the signal. Although these instruments are very useful and can be more accurate than the oscilloscope, their application is mainly limited to the measurement of one parameter of the signal. With an oscilloscope one can visualize the signal of interest and also observe whether the signal contains properties that would not be made apparent by most other instruments (for example, whether the signal is superimposed on a dc level, or whether there are noise or relative hf oscillations present with the signal at the test point). Thus the oscilloscope is a more valuable instrument because it gives an exact visual representation of the signal waveform.

Figure 1.1 shows a chart recorder drawing a graph of a signal as a function of time. Of course, the recorder can only create a replica of the signal if the pen follows the excursions of the signal exactly, and if the paper moves at a constant speed. The oscilloscope works in a similar way: The spot follows the excursions of the signal in the vertical direction and at the same time the spot is moved in the horizontal direction at a constant speed. The graph on the recorder is distorted when the paper speed does not remain constant. In the same way, the display on the oscilloscope is distorted when the ramp voltage—a voltage that increases linearly with time—is not perfectly linear. At this point, the similarity between the recorder and the oscilloscope ceases.

The recorder will draw a graph as long as paper is being transported along the pen system. In the oscilloscope we have one screen on which a part of the signal is written during a certain time span. In order to obtain a stable picture, the oscilloscope will draw a great many of those parts of the signal, one part after the other and each one covering the previous one exactly. Thus the eye observes one steady picture of the waveform. It is assumed here that the signal is repetitive in time. The method of obtaining a steady picture is discussed later in this chapter.

There is a much bigger distinction between the chart recorder and

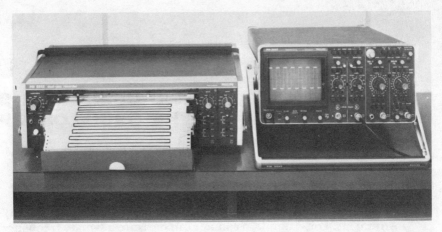

Fig. 1.1 To create an exact replica of a time-variable signal, the recorder paper speed must be constant and the oscilloscope sweep time must be linear.

the oscilloscope, however. The writing system of the recorder has a certain mass, whereas the picture on the oscilloscope screen is written with a beam of electrons that are virtually massless. Therefore, the speed of the recorder system is limited to a few transients per second, while the electron beam can visualize transients in the nanosecond (10^{-9} second) area. The oscilloscope is thus able to visualize much faster phenomena than the recorder, and it is primarily for this reason that the oscilloscope is as widely used as it is today.

1.2 THE CATHODE-RAY TUBE

The heart of the oscilloscope is the cathode-ray tube, since it performs the basic functions to convert a signal into an image; it is the output device, or display portion, of the instrument. The cathode-ray tube (CRT) is a vacuum tube similar in shape to a TV picture tube, as illustrated in Fig. 1.2. The assembly of electrodes in the narrow part of the tube is known as the *electron gun*. The electron gun furnishes a controllable source of electrons and focuses these electrons into a beam with the focus point (spot) on the screen. The beam is deflected vertically and horizontally in the deflection section before striking the layer of phosphor at the screen to produce light. The operation of the CRT can best be studied by dividing the tube into sections, referring to Fig. 1.2 and discussing each section in turn.

The Electron Gun

In the electron gun the electrons are generated by heating the cathode K, which then emits the electrons. These electrons are shaped into a beam in the gun. The intensity of the beam is controlled by the voltage between the cathode K and the Wehnelt cylinder G. If this voltage is such that no electrons arrive at the screen, the condition of the tube is called *blanked*. The electrons emitted by the cathode are brought to a first focus by means of an electrostatic field produced between the Wehnelt cylinder G and anode a_1. From this first focus, or crossover point, the beam begins to diverge until it enters a second electrostatic field between anodes a_1 and a_3 and anode a_2. Anode a_2 is the main focus electrode; by varying the potential at this point, the beam can be brought to a sharp spot on the CRT screen. Acceleration of the electrons from the cathode towards the screen is caused by the electrostatic field existing along the axis of the tube. This field is established by the difference in potential between the cathode and the interconnected electrodes a_1 and a_3, usually about 2 kV.

Deflection Sensitivity

Located between the electron gun and the screen are two pairs of *deflection plates*. These plates are so arranged that the electrical fields between each pair of plates are mutually at right angles. Under the influence of the electrical field produced between each pair of plates, the electron beam is deflected towards the plate which is at the positive potential with respect to the other. Since the same applies for the other pair of plates, it is possible to deflect the beam in two directions, that is, the X and Y coordinates of the screen. In normal operation the X deflection is generated

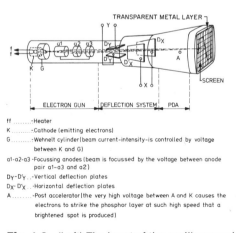

ff ....-Heater
K ....:Cathode (emitting electrons)
G ....:Wehnelt cylinder (beam current-intensity-is controlled by voltage between K and G)
a1-a2-a3 -Focussing anodes (beam is focussed by the voltage between anode pair a1-a3 and a2)
Dy-D'y ..-Vertical deflection plates
Dx-D'x ...-Horizontal deflection plates
A ....-Post accelerator (the very high voltage between A and K causes the electrons to strike the phosphor layer at such high speed that a brightened spot is produced)

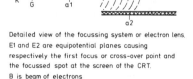

Detailed view of the focussing system or electron lens.
E1 and E2 are equipotential planes causing respectively the first focus or cross-over point and the focussed spot at the screen of the CRT.
B is beam of electrons

Fig. 1.2 (Left) The heart of the oscilloscope is the cathode-ray tube. This illustration shows the tube construction and identifies the essential parts. (Right) Detailed view of the focusing system or electron lens. E_1 and E_2 are equipotential planes causing the first focus or crossover point, and the focused spot at the screen of the CRT. B is the electron beam.

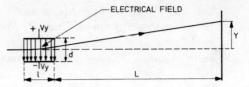

Fig. 1.3a The electrical field causes the electrons to be deflected towards the positively charged plate.

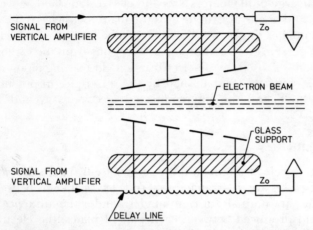

Fig. 1.3b Segmented deflection plates increase the bandwidth of CRTs.

within the instrument in the form of a repetitive left-to-right sweep across the screen, while the signal to be measured produces the Y deflection.

The deflection sensitivity (DS) establishes the number of centimeters of deflection on the screen per volt of deflection voltage between the plates. Referring to Figs. 1.2 and 1.3A, it can be derived that

$$DS = \frac{Y}{V_y} = \frac{1 \cdot L}{2 \cdot d \cdot V_z} \quad cm/V$$

In this expression, V_z is the difference in potential which the electrons pass from the cathode through the electron gun as far as the deflection plates (for example, $V_z = 2$ kV).

Segmented Deflection Plates

In high-frequency oscilloscopes the vertical deflection plates may be segmented (see Fig. 1.3B). The object of this type of CRT is explained in the following paragraphs.

With normal deflection plates the electrons of the beam may remain so long between the plates that high-frequency signal transitions occur during the time the electrons travel along the deflection path. The effect on the deflection of the beam would then be less than the input signal requires, or less than on low-frequency signals.

By segmenting the deflection plates, a specific drive per deflection segment may be obtained, resulting in a proper deflection of high-frequency signals. In this case the stray capacitances between the plates are used to form a delay line together with the externally connected coils. The delay line is terminated by its characteristic impedance Z_0. In this way the propagation of the electrical signal through the delay line toward the termination takes somewhat more time.

By matching the propagation velocity in the delay line to the velocity of the electron beam between the plates, each electron is forced by the same phase of the signal at each segment, resulting in a constant deflection sensitivity of all frequencies within the CRT's (increased) bandwidth.

The PDA System

Referring to Fig. 1.2, the next section towards the screen is the *postacceleration area*. Not every tube in use today has acceleration. This depends on the highest sweep frequencies to be supplied to the tube; for the tube this means the highest writing speed to be displayed. For time coefficients up to 0.1 μs/div no postacceleration is needed. Thus, 10-MHz sine waves arc displayed with 1 period per division. In this case the inside of the tube from the deflection plates to almost as far as the screen is covered with a conductive coating of Aquadag. The Aquadag coating is connected to anodes a_1 and a_3 at 0-V potential. This kind of tube is called a *monoaccelerator tube,* because after the electrons pass anode a_3 no acceleration forces are applied to them. In order to raise the writing speed, anodes a_1 and a_3 in the monoaccelerator can be brought to a potential of approximately 4 kV. But as can be seen from the relation of the deflection sensitivity (DS), it follows that increasing V_z from 2 to 4 kV causes the DS to decrease proportionally.

In order to overcome the problem of the writing speed, postdeflection acceleration (PDA) is applied. This method allows the focusing and deflection sections to be operated at even lower voltages than the monoaccelerator tube. These lower operating voltages reduce the velocity of the beam in the deflection system and are an aid to better deflection sensitivity. After the beam has been deflected, it is then accelerated in the postacceleration area to give a high light output.

However, there are some disadvantages with postacceleration, which can be better understood if we consider the successive developments that have taken place in the past decade.

First, instead of the Aquadag coating used in the monoaccelerator, a continuous electron lens over the entire funnel of the tube is constructed

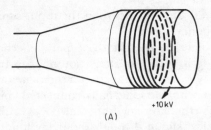

(A)

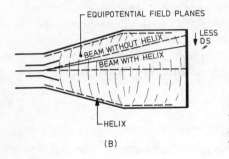

(B)

Fig. 1.4 (A) The helically-wound resistive material used for the post-deflection acceleration system. (B) The influence of the helix on the deflection sensitivity (DS).

from resistive material that is helically wound (Fig. 1.4A). The applied acceleration voltage is about 10 kV with respect to the cathode. A disadvantage of this system is that the electrical field is converging, thus moving the electrons towards the center of the screen. Thus the light output was improved at the expense of the deflection sensitivity (Fig. 1.4B). This type of CRT is seldom used today.

The compression of the helix PDA tube can be eliminated by a mesh located in the CRT just beyond the deflection plates. Now the converging field can even be transferred into a diverging one, using a continuous conductive layer similar to Aquadag for PDA. However, the mesh is a metal electrode, and as a result of the voltage applied to it (see Fig. 1.5) will intercept 30 to 50% of the beam electrons, thereby again reducing the light output. Another disadvantage of the mesh tube is that the spot size is increased, compared to the helix PDA tube. The helix field is

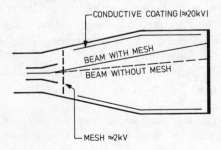

Fig. 1.5 A mesh placed into the helix increases the deflection sensitivity.

converging, which reduces the DS; but also, the beam is compressed and consequently the spot size is reduced.

To overcome the problems of the mesh tube, but mainly the problem of reduced light output, the PDA voltage has been increased to about 20 kV, which also compresses the beam somewhat, resulting in a slightly smaller spot size again. To further increase the deflection sensitivity, the helix has become domed (see Fig. 1.6). The gain in DS is even such that the CRT can be shortened and still retain an acceptable DS. Shortening the CRT is an important factor in reducing the overall size of an instrument. An equally important factor in reducing the size of an instrument is the application of integrated circuits.

The Screen

The last section illustrated in Fig. 1.2 is the *screen*. The beam of electrons, brought to a focus at the screen, is invisible. The screen is coated internally with phosphor, which emits light on the spot where the electron beam hits it. The color of the radiation and the duration of the "afterglow" depend on the type of phosphor used. After the phosphor layer is applied to the screen, a very thin metal layer may be vaporized over the phosphor (Fig. 1.2). This metal layer is transparent to the electron beam and acts as a heat sink for the heat developed in the generation of light in the phosphor. Without this transparent metal layer the phosphor could be burned away by the high energy of the electron beam, after which no radiation of light would be possible. Another very important advantage of the metal layer is that the light is reflected to a certain extent, resulting in a higher light output on the screen.

In order to take measurements by means of the screen, a graticule has to be placed in front of it. This *external graticule* gives rise to parallax in the readout because it is not in the same plane as the phosphor. However, the external graticule can easily be removed for other types of measurements, for example, *X-Y* measurements.

To overcome the problem of parallax, *internal graticules* may be pro-

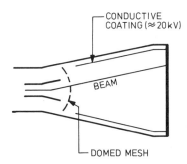

CONDUCTIVE
COATING (≈20 kV)

BEAM

DOMED MESH

Fig. 1.6 The use of a domed mesh permits the CRT to be made shorter in length while maintaining the increase in deflection sensitivity.

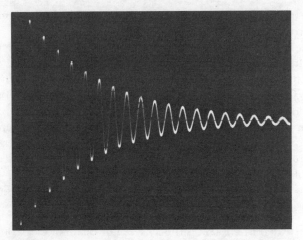

Fig. 1.7 With this single-shot display the photographic writing speed is defined.

cessed onto the internal surface of the screen, virtually in the same plane as the phosphor. The more sophisticated oscilloscopes possess internal graticules almost without exception.

Definition of Photographic Writing Speed

An important aspect of a CRT is the maximum writing speed, in other words, the maximum deflection speed which is still visible. But this depends on a great number of circumstances, including:

1. The number of pictures written per second
2. The setting of the INTENSITY control
3. The setting of the FOCUS control
4. The ambient light
5. The filter in front of the screen used to absorb ambient light
6. The subjective opinion of what is visible or not quite visible

This has led to the convention of taking a picture from the screen using a very sensitive film (usually Polaroid, about 3000 ASA). The picture on the screen must be one single sweep, at full intensity, with optimum focus, and without a filter. Consequently, the camera with which the picture is taken must be specified, together with the camera settings, the film used, and exposure details [that is, prefogging or not (prefogging means the addition of some ambient light in order to increase the film sensitivity)].

The signal used for the single shot is shown in Fig. 1.7. From the damped sine wave displayed it will be clear that the writing speed is decreasing from left to right. The first visible vertical half-sine-wave trace defines the maximum photographic writing speed.

The writing speed is calculated as shown in Fig. 1.8. The speed of the sine wave in the vertical, or Y, direction at the screen is considered as the projection on the Y axis of a spot P moving with constant angular speed at the circumference. As derived in Fig. 1.8, the maximum speed is

$$V_{Y,\text{max}} = \frac{\pi Y}{T}$$

where Y is the peak-to-peak amplitude and T is the period of the sine wave.

Refer back to Fig. 1.7 and suppose that the frequency of the damped sine wave is known to be tuned at 50 MHz ($T = 0.02\ \mu s$). The first slope visible in the picture is the one between the third top peak and the third bottom peak from the left. With reference to the oscilloscope screen, this means 5 divisions, or 5 cm.

Now the maximum photographic writing speed is calculated as

$$V_{\text{max}} = \frac{\pi \times 5}{0.02} \quad \text{cm}/\mu s$$

$$= 785 \quad \text{cm}/\mu s$$

This is a practical value as can be seen in the specifications of the 50-MHz Philips PM 3240 oscilloscope, described in Sec. 7.3.

1.3 TRIGGERING—OR HOW TO OBTAIN A STABLE DISPLAY

Apart from single-shot measurements, the signal to be measured must be repetitive. Signals a, b, and c in Fig. 1.9 are all repetitive, because a span of time can be defined such that the same signal is repeated sequen-

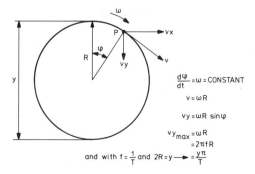

$$\frac{d\varphi}{dt} = \omega = \text{CONSTANT}$$

$$v = \omega R$$

$$v_y = \omega R \sin\varphi$$

$$v_{y_{\text{max}}} = \omega R$$

$$= 2\pi f R$$

and with $f = \frac{1}{T}$ and $2R = y \longrightarrow = \frac{y\pi}{T}$

Fig. 1.8 The derivation used to calculate the maximum photographic writing speed of cathode-ray tube.

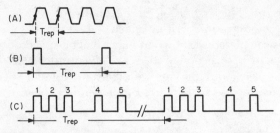

Fig. 1.9 Signals a, b, and c are all repetitive because a time span may be defined such that the same signal is repeated sequentially.

tially. The oscilloscope will obtain a stable display of these waveforms as follows:

1. Each sweep is started (triggered) at the same point on the waveform. The sweep is the horizontal deflection on the screen produced by a sawtooth voltage applied to the X-deflection plates. The sweep is triggered by a circuit which produces a trigger pulse each time the trigger signal (often taken from the input signal itself) crosses a certain voltage level. This can be on either the signal's positive or negative slope (see Fig. 1.10). The start of the waveform on the screen is thus determined by two settings of the oscilloscope front-panel controls:

   a. The LEVEL position on the waveform
   b. The SLOPE (positive or negative)

2. When the spot reaches the right-hand side of the screen (end position), it is quickly brought back to the left-hand side (start position). This is known as the *flyback* part of the sweep. During the flyback the beam is blanked. The sweep is started again by the next trigger pulse at exactly the same position where it started the previous time (see Fig. 1.11).

3. The sweep circuit ensures that *during* the sweep, including the flyback time, any other triggers at the input of the sweep circuit have no effect. This may happen if more than one waveform at the screen is displayed (see Fig. 1.12).

1.4 MAIN CONTROLS AND THEIR FUNCTIONS

The block diagram, Fig. 1.13, illustrates a basic oscilloscope, which includes an attenuator, a vertical amplifier, a trigger circuit, a sweep circuit, a horizontal amplifier, and a CRT control block. The operating control knobs, shown on appropriate blocks in the illustration, will be found on most oscilloscopes.

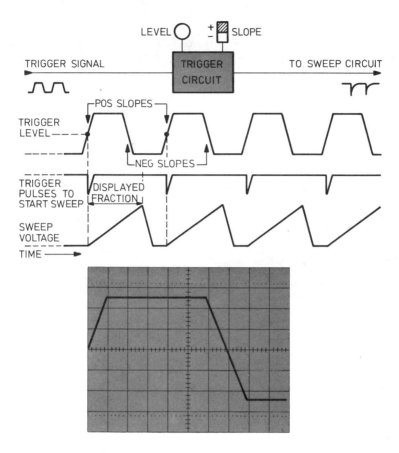

Fig. 1.10 Because each sweep starts at the same point on the waveform, a repetitive waveform is converted into a stable display. This is called *triggering.*

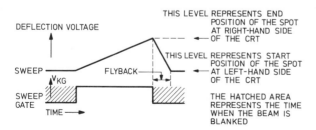

Fig. 1.11 The CRT is blanked when there is no sweep.

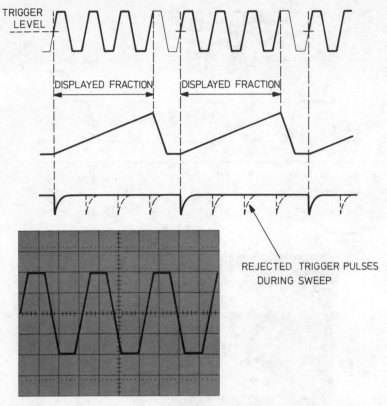

TRIGGER
LEVEL

DISPLAYED FRACTION   DISPLAYED FRACTION

REJECTED TRIGGER PULSES
DURING SWEEP

Fig. 1.12 During the sweep, the sweep and trigger circuits ensure that
any other triggers at the input of the trigger circuit have no effect.

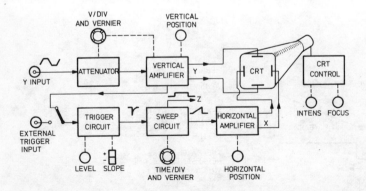

V/DIV
AND VERNIER   VERTICAL
POSITION

ATTENUATOR   VERTICAL
AMPLIFIER Y   CRT   CRT
CONTROL

Y INPUT

Z   INTENS FOCUS

EXTERNAL
TRIGGER
INPUT   TRIGGER
CIRCUIT   SWEEP
CIRCUIT   HORIZONTAL
AMPLIFIER X

LEVEL SLOPE   TIME/DIV
AND VERNIER   HORIZONTAL
POSITION

Fig. 1.13 Block diagram showing the oscilloscope's main controls.

- The ATTENUATOR and the VERTICAL AMPLIFIER enable signals, ranging from just a few millivolts to several hundred volts, to be displayed on the screen.

- Accurate amplitude measurements can be made with the V/DIV switch when the vernier is set to CAL, for example, from 10 mV/div to 10 V/div in a 1–2–5 sequence.

- The HORIZONTAL AMPLIFIER increases the generated sweep voltage to a value which will deflect the spot over the full screen.

- Accurate timing measurements can be made with the TIME/DIV switch when the vernier is set to CAL, for example, from 0.1 μs/div to 1 s/div in a 1–2–5 sequence.

- The SLOPE and LEVEL controls select that point on the waveform where the display is to start.

- An EXTERNAL TRIGGER INPUT is provided in order that a separate trigger signal, which is different from the signal to be measured, may be used to obtain the desired display.

- The FOCUS and INTENSITY controls permit a well-focused display of convenient brightness to be set on the screen.

1.5 EXERCISES

For each question circle the answer you believe is correct.

1. Refer to Fig. 1.14. With each revolution of the disk unit the index unit triggers the flip-flop and delivers an index pulse, which is measured on the oscilloscope. Due to speed variations the time between index pulses also varies by a maximum of 1%.

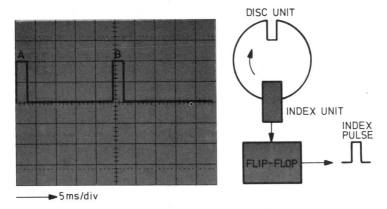

5 ms/div

Fig. 1.14 Disk measurement showing index pulse.

a. The number of revolutions per second is:

(A) 40

(B) 50

(C) 400

b. The speed variations (1% max.) will also result in time variations on the screen. The time variations will amount to:

(A)   2.5 ms

(B)   0.25 ms

(C) 250 μs

c. The time variations affect:

(A) Only pulse A in Fig. 1.14

(B) Only pulse B in Fig. 1.14

(C) Both pulses

2. Suppose we want to measure a word as shown in Fig. 1.15*A*. The oscilloscope is triggered internally, with a sweep duration as shown in Fig. 1.15*B*. What will be the effect on the display?

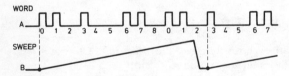

Fig. 1.15 Word measurement.

(A) This will have no particular effect and will give a stable display.

(B) The display will jump vertically.

(C) Sweeps will alternately start on different pulses, resulting in a nonrepetitive display.

3. Refer to Fig. 1.16. The pulse is measured with an oscilloscope at a TIME/DIV setting of 0.5 μs/div. The triggering controls are set for a stable display.

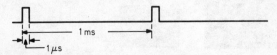

Fig. 1.16 Low repetition rate creates a display of low brightness.

a. The eye observes a stable display. Most of the time the screen is dark, resulting in a display with low brightness. The approximate proportion of time when the spot is blanked and not blanked is:

(A) 1000:1

(B) 2000:1

(C) 200:1

This exercise shows the importance of using an oscilloscope with a high light output, as obtained by postdeflection acceleration.

b. Suppose that with this measurement, the spot is only blanked during the flyback part of the sweep, thus unblanked during the sweep time only. Which of the following is true.

(A) The result would be a brightened spot at the start of the sweep.

(B) This would have no effect on the display.

(C) The total display would become much brighter.

4. The mesh in a cathode-ray tube provides:

(A) Better focusing

(B) Shorter tube

(C) More brightness

ADDITIONAL FEATURES
AND THEIR FUNCTIONS

In the previous chapter the basic operation of the oscilloscope was discussed and the fundamental control functions were shown in Fig. 1.13. However, not all signals to be measured are as simple as those shown in Figs. 1.10 and 1.12. In practice all kinds of waveforms occur, repetitive and nonrepetitive. In order to be able to handle virtually every possible signal, the oscilloscope has been developed into an instrument providing many more facilities than those mentioned. This chapter sets out to explain all these control features.

2.1 AC AND DC INPUT COUPLING

Today almost every oscilloscope is provided with a switch to select ac or dc coupling of the signal to the oscilloscope input stage, as a standard feature. When ac coupling is selected, the dc component of the signal is blocked by a capacitor inside the oscilloscope that is connected between the input terminal and the attenuator stage.

AC Coupling

AC coupling must be used when the intent is to block the dc component, for example, when measuring spikes and transients on a 5-V TTL supply voltage. Thus, the spikes and transients can be studied at an adequate scale (for example, 10 mV/div). With dc coupling and the same 10-mV/div setting, the +5-V level would be some 500 divisions above the screen, which is far out of the range of the vertical-position control.

However, it must be kept in mind that with ac coupling:

• One is never aware of the presence of any dc level with respect to ground.

• The lowest-frequency components of a signal are not properly transferred. This is illustrated in Fig. 2.1, which shows an example of a square wave of 57 Hz, while using ac coupling. The distortion is quite noticeable and becomes worse with lower repetition rates.

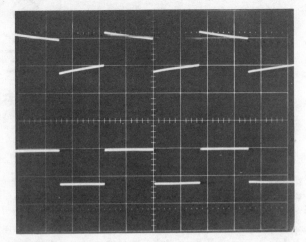

Fig. 2.1 An If pulse becomes distorted with ac input coupling (upper trace); dc coupling (lower trace) gives the correct display.

- After switching from dc to ac coupling, it takes a little time before the display has a stable vertical position.

This is quite normal and is due to the input capacitor, which must be charged to the average value of the signal.

Sometimes the input RC time is quoted in the oscilloscope specifications, with C being the series capacitor in the ac mode and R is 1 MΩ standard. If this is quoted as 20 ms, it will take approximately 100 ms before the trace is stable again.

It will be clear that dc coupling will be selected whenever possible and that the selection of ac coupling must be deliberate.

Zero Position

In the zero position of the switch the input amplifier of the oscilloscope is connected to ground, while at the same time the input bus is disconnected. This has the advantage of allowing the ground reference, or zero level, to be positioned anywhere on the screen without having to remove the signal lead.

2.2 DUAL TRACE AND DUAL BEAM

Today most oscilloscopes can display two different signals on the screen. For this purpose two vertical channels A and B, with their controls, are incorporated in the oscilloscope. Apart from comparing the amplitudes and waveforms of two time-related signals, the operator is also able to measure the time relationship between the two signals.

Two techniques can be employed to obtain the two traces on the screen: (1) a single beam is subjected to two signals by means of electronic switching (dual trace); or (2) two beams are provided to display one signal each (dual beam).

With a dual-beam oscilloscope the cathode-ray tube (CRT) may be equipped with two electron guns and two pairs of vertical deflection plates. Both deflection systems are driven by separate amplifiers (channel A and channel B) in an uninterrupted way (see the block diagram, Fig. 2.2A).

Another way to obtain a dual beam is to split the beam of a single-gun

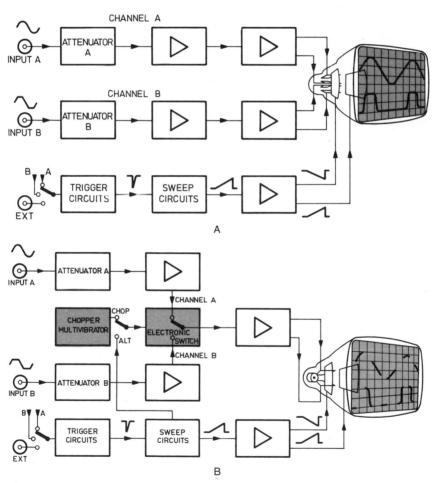

Fig. 2.2 Block diagrams illustrating dual-beam and dual-trace techniques. (*A*) The dual-beam oscilloscope provides an uninterrupted display of two waveforms. The two beams may be obtained in the tube by means of a split-beam technique. (*B*) The dual-trace oscilloscope uses a single-gun CRT and electronic switching techniques (chopped or alternate) to obtain the two waveforms.

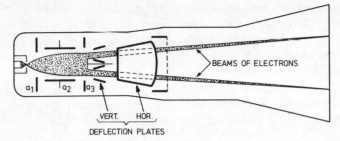

Fig. 2.3 Construction of a split-beam CRT.

CRT into two beams. After the split-up each beam is deflected by a separate pair of vertical deflection plates (see Fig. 2.3). This technology is known as the *split-beam CRT*.

With the dual-trace oscilloscope, a single-gun CRT with one pair of vertical plates is used. The final Y amplifier, providing the deflection voltage to the plates, is alternately connected to the two signals by electronic switching.

Figure 2.2*B* shows the block diagram of a dual-trace oscilloscope. The electronic switch is operated either by a free-running multivibrator or by a pulse coming from the time-base circuits, respectively, in the chopped mode or in the alternate mode. The alternate-mode pulse coming from the time-base circuits coincides with the end of the successive sweeps.

Figure 2.4 shows how the display of two input signals is affected by these techniques. The dual-beam display shows simultaneously an uninterrupted reproduction of the two signals. In the dual-trace chopped mode both waveforms are actually chopped at a rate of say 200 kHz to 1 MHz. For time coefficients less than 0.1 ms/div, this is not visible. At higher rates than this, the operator might observe a kind of display as shown in Fig. 2.2*B*. The alternate display shows that only one signal is displayed during a sweep. At the end of the first sweep the electronic switch causes the second signal to be displayed, and so on.

As the succeeding sweeps can appear very fast (depending on the time-base setting), apparently one picture with two signals can appear on the screen. These time-sharing techniques (chopped and alternate) can be easily extended to more than two channels, as in the case of a four-channel oscilloscope.

From an ergonomic point of view the dual-beam (or split-beam) oscilloscope is more convenient because no selection of switching modes has to be made and there can be no ambiguity in interpretation. Unfortunately, the construction of dual-beam and split-beam CRTs is more complicated than the construction of single-gun CRTs and hence more expensive.

2.3 SELECTION OF CHOPPED OR ALTERNATE MODE

In some of the simpler oscilloscopes the chopped or alternate mode is automatically selected by the TIME/DIV switch. The sweep speed above which the mode is switched from chopped to alternate is about 0.1 ms/div. The reason for this is obvious: with low repetition rates in the alternate mode the operator sees the traces being written one after the other. Thus, in this case the chopped mode is the better solution. At higher repetition rates the chopper frequency might interfere with the signal frequency; consequently, the alternate mode is now the better solution. Moreover, in this case the alternating process is so fast that the operator sees two signals on the screen simultaneously. With the more advanced oscilloscopes the operator can select the mode. To evaluate the best choice of mode selection, let us consider the effects of three ranges of the sweep as selected by the TIME/DIV switch.

Sweep Speeds Lower than 10 ms/div

In the alternate mode the eye observes the waveforms being written one after the other. It therefore becomes very difficult to compare the waveforms. For these sweep speeds the chopped mode must be used, as the two traces are apparently written simultaneously per sweep. The chopper frequency is so high that the chopping effect is not visible.

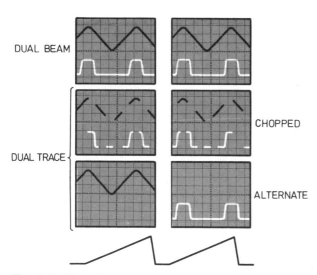

Fig. 2.4 The effects of dual-beam and dual-trace techniques on the waveforms of two input signals.

Sweep Speeds Ranging from 10 to 0.1 ms/div

Both modes may be used. However, the chopped mode is preferred, because the alternate mode gives a somewhat flickering display, which is irritating to view.

Sweep Speeds Faster than 0.1 ms/div

The alternate mode should be selected, because in the chopped mode the chopping effect may become visible on the screen. This is particularly so when the frequency of the input signal and the chopper frequency are closely related. Trigger errors which might occur in these modes, resulting in a wrong display, are discussed in Chap. 5.

2.4 DIFFERENTIAL MODE (A − B)

Oscilloscopes provided with an ADD function are able to add algebraically the two input signals A and B. If the instruments are also provided with a NORMAL/INVERT function, the signals can also be inverted in polarity or phase. Combining the two functions ADD and INVERT can lead to the possibilities:

$$A + B, A - B, B - A, \text{ and } -A - B$$

Basically it is thus possible to make differential measurements, for example, $A - B$, by using the ADD function and the INVERT function of channel B. This can be useful to reject common-mode voltages.

Signal sources, of which both terminals are floating with respect to ground, may carry a voltage with respect to ground on both terminals. This unwanted voltage is called the *common-mode voltage*. By measuring signals in the differential mode, the common-mode voltages are rejected and only the signal of interest remains. These signals are found, for example, in computer environments, in medical systems, in audio amplifiers, and in instrumentation amplifiers. Two instances of where the differential mode could be particularly beneficial are:

- In signal-tracing circuits where the signal ground is raised to a dc level. Suppose that, for proper display, dc coupling is desired for both channels. Measurements in the $A - B$ mode eliminate the dc voltage and only the signal of interest is displayed on the screen.

- In measurements of circuits where ground loops introduce hum interference on both terminals of the signal to be measured. In most cases the use of the $A - B$ mode will substantially reduce the interfering hum voltage.

Figure 2.5 shows two signals containing a common-mode hum component which is almost eliminated by the subtraction. The common-mode rejection in this example is 10.

Adjusting the Oscilloscope for *A − B* Measurements

The oscilloscope does not function as a perfect differential amplifier because the subtraction is made after a few stages of vertical attenuation and amplification instead of at the input. The degree of common-mode rejection which can be attained is greatly dependent upon how well the operator equalizes the channels before the subtraction stage. The following operation information applies:

- Use the same input coupling (ac or dc) and deflection coefficients (AMPL or V/DIV) for both channels.

- If a common-mode rejection greater than 10 is required, equalize the channels in the following way: Connect both probes from channel *A* and *B* inputs to one of the signals to be measured. Adjust GAIN (adjustment on front) or amplitude vernier of one channel, and also the probe compensation if a 10 : 1 probe is used, for minimum deflection on the screen.

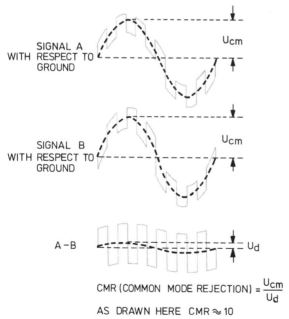

$$\text{CMR (COMMON MODE REJECTION)} = \frac{U_{cm}}{U_d}$$

AS DRAWN HERE CMR ≈ 10

Fig. 2.5 Common-mode signals that cause disturbance can be suppressed by using the *A − B* mode.

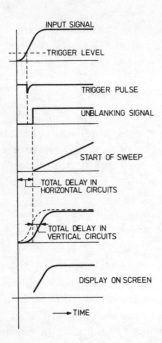

INPUT SIGNAL

--|-/---TRIGGER LEVEL

TRIGGER PULSE

UNBLANKING SIGNAL

START OF SWEEP

TOTAL DELAY IN
HORIZONTAL CIRCUITS

TOTAL DELAY IN
VERTICAL CIRCUITS

DISPLAY ON SCREEN

→TIME

Fig. 2.6 The first (bottom) part of the signal cannot be displayed without using a delay line.

• Take care that the input amplifiers of the oscilloscope are not over-driven by the common-mode voltage. In some oscilloscopes this becomes apparent when the VERTICAL POSITION is changed or when the next more sensitive deflection coefficient for both channels is selected. In these cases the display shows a sudden increase in common-mode signal amplitude.

With the Philips PM 3260 and PM 3265 oscilloscopes, for example, a common-mode rejection of at least 100 is guaranteed, provided the foregoing measures have been taken. However, it must be borne in mind that this figure is only valid for average frequencies and not at the extremes of the bandwidth.

2.5 DELAY LINE: OBSERVATION OF TRANSITIONS

The display of the oscilloscope is a plot of voltage versus time. The horizontal direction represents time, and may be regarded as a time window through which the waveform can be seen. Its length is determined by the length of the sweep (number of divisions) and the TIME/DIV setting. With a sweep length of 10 divisions and a TIME/DIV setting of 1 ms/div, we look through a time window of 10 ms. But where does this time window start in relation to the waveform?

We already know that to stabilize the display we need to start the horizontal movement of the spot on the screen at the same level of the waveform each time. The device that initiates the action for the horizontal movement is the trigger circuit. For this it may receive a fraction of the input signal. The trigger circuit produces an output pulse when the input signal goes through some selected level. The trigger output pulse activates the sweep circuit to start a horizontal sweep of the spot (see Fig. 1.10). Thus, each horizontal trace starts when the input signal goes through the selected point on its waveform, and it is not possible to display before this time.

In addition, the horizontal movement is only started some time after the trigger point on the signal, because the trigger circuit itself also takes a measurable time to get started. Furthermore, the time-base generator also generates an "unblanking pulse" (Z pulse in Fig. 1.13), enabling the CRT to give a visible spot on its screen. The enabling action also takes a little time. However, these settling times of the trigger and time-base circuits are on the order of only a few nanoseconds.

Normally there is also some delay in the vertical channel, but this is less than the delay in the horizontal circuits. The overall effect will be that the first section of the input signal cannot be visualized in this way (see Fig. 2.6).

To overcome this disadvantage, an extra time delay is included in the vertical channel. This must be between the trigger pick-off point and the CRT. This delay time is given to the input signal path before the signal enters the CRT and could take the form of an actual or artificial transmission line. An artificial transmission line consists of a piece of printed circuit board with a meander pattern on each side, as illustrated in Fig. 2.7.

Both patterns are located in such a way as to support each other's contribution to the magnetic field. As the circuit board can be made rather thin, there will be a strong coupling between the two meander patterns. This leads to a long delay/volume, because in general the propagation velocity v of a lossless delay line is

$$v = \frac{1}{\sqrt{LC}}$$

where L and C are the specific inductance and capacitance per meter transmission line.

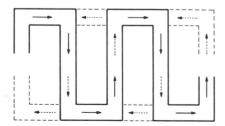

Fig. 2.7 The printed-circuit delay line; the current on the underside (light arrows) supports the current on the top side (dark arrows) to build up a magnetic field.

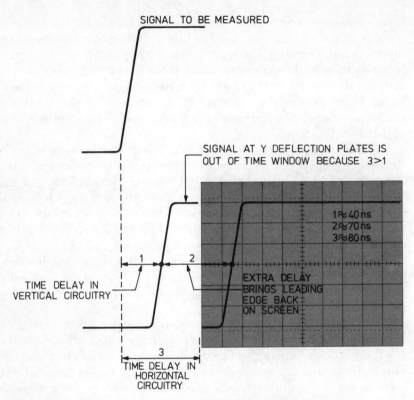

Fig. 2.8 The delay line brings the leading edge back onto the screen.

Thus with a large L and a large C, the propagation velocity becomes low and the delay time increases as a consequence. The advantage of a printed-circuit delay line is that it occupies less space than an actual transmission line consisting of a normal coaxial cable and it weighs less.

Fig. 2.8 shows how the extra delay line in the vertical channel ensures that the leading edge is brought back on the screen again. The overall result is that the sweep now starts some 20 to 30 ns before the start of the leading edge. This is of importance when it is desired to measure the shape or rise time of the leading edge (see Chap. 5). The implementation of the delay line in the oscilloscope is demonstrated in Fig. 2.9.

2.6 TRIGGER SOURCE SELECTION

Most oscilloscopes are fitted with a switch to select the trigger source. In the case of a single-channel oscilloscope this switch will have two positions: INT for internal triggering, and EXT for external triggering. In the INT mode, part of the signal is taken off from the input amplifier.

With multichannel oscilloscopes the operator can select channel A, channel *B*, etc., as trigger sources. Often a line-frequency trigger source is provided on single-channel and multichannel instruments as well as EXT. It is important to have a proper understanding of which trigger source is most suitable for a particular measurement. This is especially true when making multichannel and time-difference measurements.

With internal triggering an internal trigger signal is derived from the vertical amplifier and switched to the input of the trigger circuits. Figure 2.9 shows the vertical-amplifier stages, their relevant controls, and two points to pick off the signal for internal triggering. Trigger point 1 is taken off from the preamplifier in order to maintain good sensitivity. Internal triggering is influenced by the setting of the AMPL/DIV switch and the AC/DC switch, but is not affected by any of the other vertical controls.

For general applications internal triggering is more convenient, because it does not require any extra connections. On the other hand, using external triggering makes triggering independent of vertical controls (amplitude setting and input coupling) and the input signal itself. This is especially helpful in tracing many time-related signals, as is often the case in fault-finding digital circuitry.

Note: To measure two or more signals which are multiples of each other's frequencies, such as signals coming from different counter stages, select the signal with the *lowest repetition rate* as the trigger source. Not doing so may cause double pictures in the chopped mode or a shifted time relationship in the alternate mode.

If only a one-channel oscilloscope is available, time measurements can be made if the EXT trigger input is used, measuring both signals sequentially and using one of them for external triggering.

When LINE or MAINS is selected, a voltage derived from the power-line voltage is used as a trigger source. Mains triggering is of particular interest when it is suspected that there is a hum superimposed on the signal. Triggering from the line voltage results in a picture where multiples of the line frequency provide a stable display. For example, it can be de-

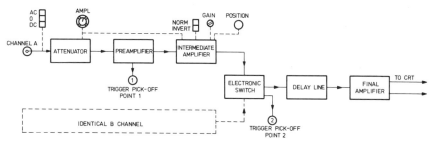

Fig. 2.9 Internal-trigger pick-off points have alternative applications.

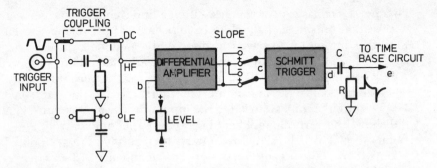

Fig. 2.10 Block diagram of a trigger circuit showing the relevant controls.

cided now whether a kind of amplitude modulation present on the signal originates from hum or from some other source.

Some oscilloscopes do have the facility to select *composite triggering* (point 2, Fig. 2.9). Composite triggering has some interesting, though limited, applications. In the alternate mode it is normally only possible to compare signals which are related in frequency. Composite triggering makes it possible to obtain a stable picture of two signals which are unrelated in frequency, because with each sweep the trigger signal is also switched to the other channel. For example, it is possible to apply an accurate timing signal to channel A, apply the unrelated signal to be measured to channel B, and obtain a stable display for the comparison of the two signals (see Chap. 6, Measuring Examples).

Another useful application is in the differential mode ($A - B$ measurements, Sec. 2.4). It is not only possible to display the difference of two signals, but in the composite trigger mode, triggering may occur also on the difference signal. Any instability in triggering due to common-mode voltages present in both signals A and B is considerably reduced by triggering on the difference signal in which the common-mode signal is strongly reduced.

Note: If the oscilloscope possesses the facility for X-Y measurement, then various sources may be used for horizontal, or X, deflection. In this case the signal is not used for trigger purposes but is directly fed to the horizontal amplifier for further amplification and X deflection. The time-base generator is automatically switched off in this case.

2.7 TRIGGER COUPLING, LEVEL, AND SLOPE

We have seen how one of the input signals or an external signal is selected for triggering purposes. However, if desired, the selected trigger signal can be filtered first (high pass or low pass) before being routed to a

Schmitt trigger. The output signal of this component is used (after differentiating) to trigger the time-base generator.

Why is this filter circuit added? The signal to be displayed may contain unwanted hum, noise, hf spurious, etc. If this signal is fed directly to the Schmitt trigger, it can produce unwanted pulses. In this case it would be impossible to obtain a stable picture on the screen. For this reason frequency filters may be switched into the circuit to affect the transfer characteristic, removing the interfering frequency components from the trigger signal and resulting in a more stable picture. A block diagram of the trigger circuit is shown in Fig. 2.10. The relevant controls are indicated in the appropriate blocks. The illustration also shows the basic coupling filters. The crossover frequencies of the filters are usually the same, resulting in a frequency bandpass as shown in Fig. 2.11A, where the crossover frequency is 50 kHz.

When using the coupling switch, dc coupling should be used whenever possible. Only for the previous reasons should lf or hf coupling be used. For example, in the hf position the trigger signal is ac-coupled to

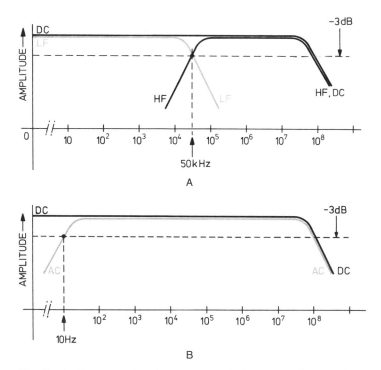

Fig. 2.11 Frequency bandpass curves of trigger coupling circuits. (*A*) Frequency responses for dc, lf, and hf trigger coupling. (*B*) Frequency responses for dc and ac trigger coupling.

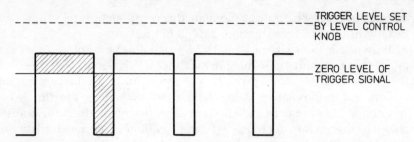

Fig. 2.12   No trigger pulses are generated when the signal is ac- or hf-coupled.

the next stage, as can be seen in Fig. 2.10. As a result it could be possible that the trigger signal does not reach the level set by the LEVEL control knob of the next stage, so that no trigger pulses would be generated. In such a case there will be no trace on the screen. This example is illustrated in Fig. 2.12.

Note: It is supposed here that at the Y input the signal is dc-coupled; otherwise, the effect shown in Fig. 2.12 would still occur.

Next to the trigger-coupling circuits is a differential-amplifier stage. This amplifier has a very small dynamic range. The trigger signal, which is fed to one input of the differential amplifier, is converted into a near square-wave output voltage. A dc voltage is applied to the other input of the differential amplifier. By varying this dc voltage (LEVEL), the position of the dynamic range is shifted with respect to the trigger signal such that the level control can be realized. From Fig. 2.13A it can be seen that the sweep is started at the negative slope of the trigger. In order to be able to trigger also at the upward or positive slope of the signal a selection switch is placed between the outputs of the differential amplifier and the input of the Schmitt trigger (Fig. 2.10).

Note that only the trigger signal is inverted here, which should not be confused with the signal in the Y channel to the screen. Two more trigger-level settings are demonstrated in Fig. 2.13B and C. A differentiating RC circuit at the Schmitt trigger output provides the fast spike pulses to start the sweep (see Fig. 2.10).

Summarizing, the following general rules apply when using the coupling switch:

- Select dc coupling for all general-purpose applications. It may provide correct triggering at all frequencies. The level at which the sweep starts is not affected by the trigger waveform or frequency.

- Select hf coupling if unwanted lf components are to be suppressed, for example, hum.

• Select lf coupling to reject noise if this disturbs the stability of the triggering.

Those oscilloscopes which are not provided with hf-lf-dc trigger coupling can normally be ac- or dc-coupled only. The dc mode is the same as has been described. The ac mode has a filter similar to that described for the hf mode, but the crossover frequency of the filter is much lower, about 10 Hz. Here the ac mode is intended only to block any dc content in the trigger signal (Fig. 2.11*B*).

2.8 AUTOMATIC TRIGGER-LEVEL CONTROL AND TRIGGER SENSITIVITY

From the previous section it will be clear that a stable picture can only be obtained if the trigger level is set within the peak-to-peak value of the trigger signal. The trigger-level control normally has a fixed range. From Fig. 2.10 it can be seen that this range is determined by the voltage across the LEVEL potentiometer at the lower input terminal of the differential amplifier.

For ease of operation the LEVEL control may be made nonlinear, for example, as in the Philips PM 3240 and PM 3260 series of oscilloscopes. Figure 2.14 shows that the range per degree of rotation is much smaller in the midsection of the scale than it is at the ends of the scale, making the trigger-level setting in the middle of the screen much easier. It is good practice to start measurements with the LEVEL control in its middle position, because a trigger level of 0 V normally provides stable triggering.

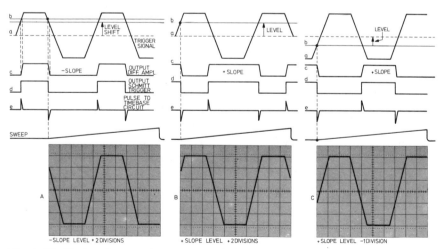

Fig. 2.13 Timing diagram showing the effect of the trigger controls on the start of the display.

Fig. 2.14 LEVEL control: the range per degree of rotation is smaller in the midsection of the scale than it is at the ends of the scale. The indicated values are scale divisions in the internal trigger mode.

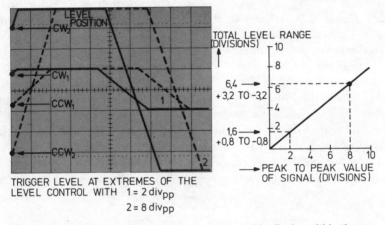

TRIGGER LEVEL AT EXTREMES OF THE
LEVEL CONTROL WITH   1 = 2 div$_{pp}$
                     2 = 8 div$_{pp}$

Fig. 2.15 AUTO LEVEL range always assures a stable display within the entire LEVEL range.

Another method of simplifying the setting of the trigger level is to detect the peak-to-peak value of the applied trigger voltage and to use this voltage to set the level range. In the Philips PM 3232, PM 3233, and PM 3234 oscilloscopes such a circuit is provided. The peak-to-peak detector measures the peak values of the trigger signal and supplies somewhat smaller voltages to the LEVEL potentiometer, which determines the range. The result is illustrated in Fig. 2.15. With a 2-division signal on the screen, the LEVEL control is adjustable from + 0.8 division fully clockwise (cw) to − 0.8 division fully counterclockwise (ccw), thus having the total range of 1.6 divisions. With an 8-division signal, the LEVEL control is adjustable from + 3.2 divisions (cw) to − 3.2 divisions (ccw). Even for small signals (down to 1 division), stable triggering can be attained at any LEVEL position. It will be appreciated that when working with small signals the peak-to-peak detector circuit also enables the operator to set the LEVEL control more easily. Because of bandwidth limitations the automatic trigger-level circuit has not yet been incorporated in all oscilloscopes.

A variation of this method of automatic triggering is to detect the peak or top value of the trigger signal and to use a somewhat smaller value as a fixed LEVEL setting. This kind of level setting is indicated as TOP triggering (as in, for example, Philips PM 3225 and PM 3226 oscilloscopes).

Thus far, only the means of setting the level for internal triggering have been discussed. The level is expressed in divisions on the screen. The minimum number of divisions at which proper triggering occurs is called the *trigger sensitivity*. As explained in Sec. 2.6, external triggering makes the triggering independent of the vertical-input-channel control settings (amplitude setting and input coupling). For this reason the trigger sensitivity for external triggering is expressed directly in volts (for example, ≤ 150 mV). In other words the trigger voltage applied to the EXT TRIG input bus can be as low as 150 mV to obtain proper triggering.

2.9 THE TIME-BASE CIRCUIT

Figure 2.16 shows a somewhat extended block diagram of the time-base circuit. For a linear time scale on the screen, a linearly increasing ramp voltage is needed to produce a sweep. This voltage is generated by charging a capacitor with a constant current. This is called the *integrator*.

Negative spikes from the trigger circuit arrive at the sweep-gating multivibrator (SGM), which is, in fact, a Schmitt trigger. The output from the SGM is used to switch the integrator on and off. The integrator output is used to provide the X deflection and to feed the hold-off circuit. The hold-off pulse resets the SGM and prevents it from responding to trigger pulses before the time-base capacitor has fully discharged. Referring to Fig. 2.17, at t_1 a trigger pulse activates the SGM, producing a

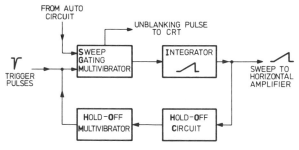

Fig. 2.16 A somewhat extended block diagram of a time-base circuit.

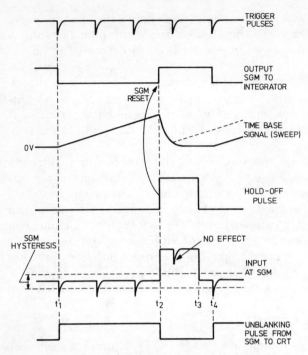

Fig. 2.17 The hold-off time prevents triggers from interfering with the start of the sweep.

linear ramp voltage at the integrator output. Once this time-base signal has reached a level predetermined by the hold-off circuit (Fig. 2.16), the hold-off multivibrator is switched over (t_2). This causes the SGM to reset because the hold-off multivibrator pulse shifts the input level of the SGM above the upper level of its hysteresis gap (remember that this is a Schmitt trigger). Moreover, as long as the hold-off multivibrator is set, the incoming trigger pulses cannot pass the lower hysteresis level of the SGM by which it is inhibited or held off. During the hold-off period the time-base capacitor has ample time to discharge, so that the next ramp starts from 0 V also. Failing this, the next sweep would start at a position other than its zero point (see Fig. 2.17). After the hold-off period (t_3), the first trigger pulse initiates the next time-base ramp (t_4).

During the time t_2 to t_4, the trace of the CRT is suppressed. This is called *blanking*. This is done by supplying a negative voltage at the control grid (Wehnelt cylinder) of the CRT, thereby cutting off the electron beam. During the time-base signal, a positive pulse is superimposed on this dc level, allowing the beam of electrons to pass. This pulse is called the "unblanking" pulse and is derived from the SGM output (see Figs.

2.16 and 1.11). The following paragraphs describe special operating modes of the time-base circuit.

2.10 TRIGGER MODES: AUTO AND SINGLE

From the previous paragraphs it will be clear that if no signal is present at the input of the oscilloscope, no trigger pulses are generated and the CRT is blanked (Fig. 2.17). Consequently, there is nothing to observe on the screen. But this may also be the case if the signal to the trigger circuit (Fig. 2.10) does not reach the trigger level, again resulting in no trigger pulses being generated. Thus, from the screen it cannot be decided whether there is no signal at the Y input, or whether the oscilloscope is not being triggered in the right way.

To overcome this problem, an auto-trigger circuit may be built into the oscilloscope. This circuit ensures that the time-base circuit is also started, in the absence of trigger pulses, so that a trace is always visible on the screen. The operation of the oscilloscope can now be verified and the controls set without having to apply an external signal or set the LEVEL control.

In the AUTO mode the time-base circuit is switched to a free-running state by the auto circuit, a fraction of a second (0.2 to 0.5 s) after the last trigger pulse. Now sweeps are produced in the AUTO–free-running mode. As soon as the first trigger pulse arrives, the AUTO circuit is switched back to its original (inoperative) state and the time-base circuit is triggered again as in the normal trigger (TRIG) mode (Fig. 2.18). It will be clear that the AUTO mode cannot be used for signals with very low repetition rates.

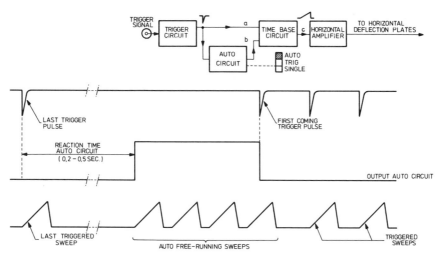

Fig. 2.18 AUTO mode provides sweeps in the absence of trigger signals.

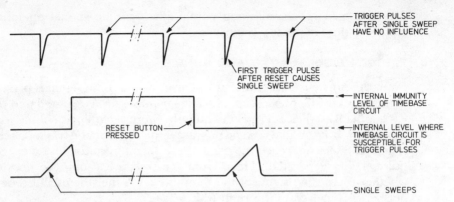

TRIGGER PULSES
AFTER SINGLE SWEEP
HAVE NO INFLUENCE

FIRST TRIGGER PULSE
AFTER RESET CAUSES
SINGLE SWEEP

INTERNAL IMMUNITY
LEVEL OF TIMEBASE
CIRCUIT

RESET BUTTON
PRESSED

INTERNAL LEVEL WHERE
TIMEBASE CIRCUIT IS
SUSCEPTIBLE FOR
TRIGGER PULSES

SINGLE SWEEPS

Fig. 2.19 In the SINGLE mode position the time base is switched so that it will not accept any other trigger pulses after the last single sweep.

Two simple rules apply to the use of the AUTO or triggered (TRIG) mode:

• Use the AUTO mode for all normal applications. This will provide a reference trace on the screen when there is no signal applied or when the LEVEL control is wrongly set.

• Use the trigger (TRIG) mode for low-repetition-rate signals (lower than 10 Hz, for example).

The SINGLE sweep mode is intended for nonrepetitive waveforms. When the signals to be measured occur randomly in time, they cannot be studied from the screen at a very low average repetition. In such cases it is common practice to take a photograph of the signal from the screen, using a polaroid film. To take a photograph, it is necessary that one sweep, and only one sweep, be written on the screen, even though more trigger pulses may be produced after the first pulse. For this purpose, the trigger mode switch might have a third position, SINGLE, besides the normal TRIG and AUTO positions.

In the SINGLE mode position the time-base circuit is switched such that no other trigger pulses will be accepted after the last single sweep. This is accomplished by switching the level (hold-off) internally at the end of the sweep (Fig. 2.19).

The time-base circuit will only accept trigger pulses when the RESET push-button has been depressed, and the time base will be triggered by the first incoming trigger pulse. At the end of this single sweep the hold-off level remains activated. For further sweeps the RESET button has to be depressed again.

2.11 VARIABLE HOLD-OFF PERIOD

Suppose a series of double pulses have to be displayed, as shown in Fig. 2.20*A*. The end of the first time-base ramp is reached after pulse 5 and the end of the hold-off period is reached before pulse 6. The second sweep will then be triggered at pulse 6 (Fig. 2.20*C*). This means that the following pulses appear at the screen, as shown in Fig. 2.20*E*. The result of this is shown in Fig. 2.20*G*, which is erroneous. By making the hold-off period longer, the second sweep will be triggered by pulse 7. As a result the waveforms during the first and second sweeps will coincide, and the proper picture will be obtained as illustrated in Fig. 2.21 and the display is in accordance with Fig. 2.20*A*.

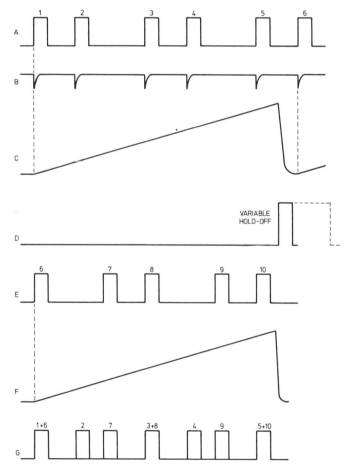

Fig. 2.20 Timing diagram showing the effects of VARIABLE HOLD-OFF.

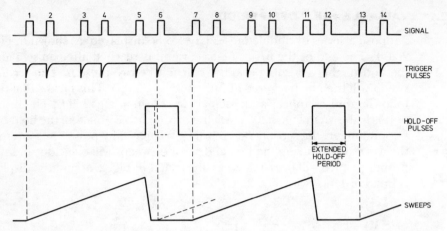

Fig. 2.21 VARIABLE HOLD-OFF permits the sweep to be triggered each time at the first pulse of a double-pulse signal.

The same result could have been obtained by shortening the time-base sweep by means of the vernier control, but then the time scale would no longer be calibrated. For this reason a variable hold-off control is sometimes built into an oscilloscope. However, relatively few oscilloscopes possess this feature, such as the Philips PM 3260 and PM 3265.

The hold-off time must be related to the time-base sweep speed. If not, at high sweep speeds the hold-off time would be too long, and the successive sweeps will appear only after a relatively long time. Consequently, a fast sweep would be displayed at a low repetition rate, which would reduce the light output (brightness) to a large extent. For this reason the range of the hold-off time is automatically set appropriately with the TIME/DIV switch.

2.12 TIME-BASE MAGNIFIER

Most oscilloscopes are provided with a magnifier switch to enable the display to be magnified along the time axis by a fixed factor, usually 5 or 10. Magnification is achieved by increasing the amplification of the horizontal amplifier (Fig. 2.25). The amount of magnification is limited to 5 × or 10 × because any instability in the input signal or in the horizontal channel of the oscilloscope is also magnified. Furthermore, excessive magnification makes it difficult to locate a particular part of the waveform on the screen.

As can be seen from Fig. 2.22, the expanded time scale provides a more detailed display and better resolution along the time axis. The start of the magnified display is determined by the setting of the horizontal position control, POSITION/TB MAGN, in Fig. 2.25. The magnified picture can be varied over the full range of the unmagnified sweep.

The absolute accuracy in magnified time-base measurements is somewhat reduced because the accuracy of the magnification, usually 1 to 3%, is increased to the 2 to 5% time-base accuracy. However, if pulse 3 in Fig. 2.22 is to be studied in more detail on the screen, an increase of the sweep speed to 2 μs/div would shift pulse 3 out of the picture, assuming that the sweep remains triggered at pulse 1. In this case, use of the time-base magnifier has obvious advantages.

2.13 DELAYED TIME BASE

Frequently, the operator is particularly interested in only a small part of the waveform on the screen. In Fig. 2.22 it was shown how a magnified picture, starting at an adjustable time after the start of the sweep, enabled the operator to obtain a more detailed view of any event along the time axis. However, the advantage and usefulness of a time-base magnifier is rather limited. Therefore, the more sophisticated oscilloscopes possess a delayed-time-base generator. These oscilloscopes have a second time-base circuit, whose sweep is started some time (delay time) after the start of the first sweep (main time base).

The effect of the delayed time base is illustrated in Fig. 2.23. A transient in a 16-bit word is viewed in more detail by using the delayed-time-base facility. The main time base is (externally) triggered at t_0. After some time (delay time), at about the 9th pulse, the second (delayed) time

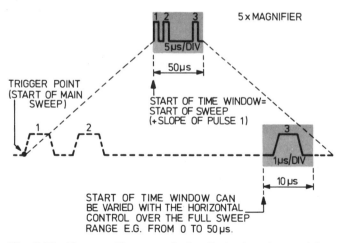

Fig. 2.22 The magnifier expands the display by a factor of five. The expanded display can be shifted over the full unmagnified sweep.

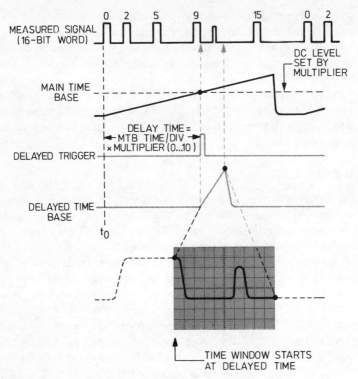

Fig. 2.23 Delayed sweep allows large magnifications to be obtained and the display start to be accurately set.

base is started. The sweep speed (TIME/DIV) of the delayed time base (DTB) is set to a higher value, resulting in magnification with respect to the main time base (MTB). The result on the screen is shown in Fig. 2.23 (switch SK in Fig. 2.25 in the "delayed" position). Thus, for this operation two things have to be done:

1. Shift the starting point of the second sweep with respect to the main sweep.

2. Set the speed of the second time-base generator to a convenient value concerning the phenomenon to be observed.

The relation of the main- and delayed-time-base generators is given in the block diagram in Fig. 2.24. Actually, the delayed-time-base circuit consists of the same circuit elements as the main-time-base circuit and is operating as the main time base in its single sweep position. In this mode the main-time-base circuit was set manually and the sweep was triggered only once by the first trigger pulse.

In the delayed time base the start of the ramp is dependent upon the comparator signal. When the ramp voltage of the main time base exceeds the voltage at the DELAY potentiometer, a trigger signal is given to a third multivibrator, the reset multivibrator (REM). This REM was set at the beginning of the main sweep by the sweep-gating multivibrator (SGM). By means of the hold-off multivibrator (HOM) of the delayed time base, the sweep-gating multivibrator (SGM) is triggered either at the same moment that the MTB sweep voltage exceeds the voltage at the DELAY potentiometer, or by a trigger pulse which is the first pulse after this moment. This depends on the position of the START/TRIG switch (Fig. 2.24).

In the START mode the delayed sweep is immediately started once the main sweep has exceeded the level of the DELAY potentiometer. In the TRIG mode the delayed time base is set ready when the main sweep exceeds the level of the DELAY potentiometer, but the delayed sweep is only started after a trigger pulse from the trigger circuit of the DTB. In Sec. 2.15 the application of the START and/or TRIG modes of the delayed time base is explained.

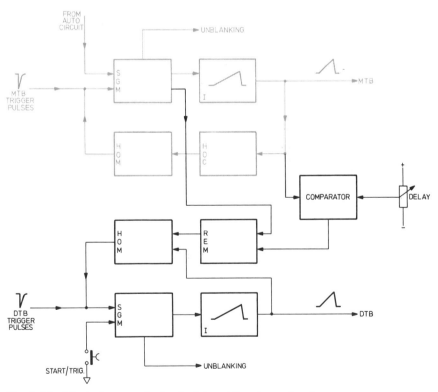

Fig. 2.24 Block diagram of a basic delayed-time-base circuit.

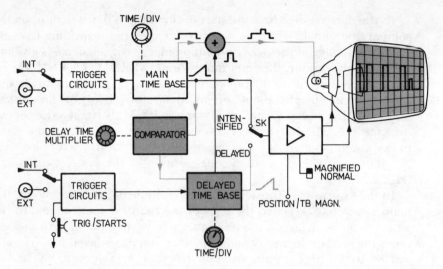

Fig. 2.25 Block diagram showing the operation of the main-time-base intensified mode and the delayed-time-base mode.

The delayed-time-base trigger circuit is identical to that of the main time base, including the same trigger coupling and trigger source selection possibilities, with the exception of MAINS triggering.

As can be seen from Fig. 2.24 the comparator compares the dc voltage from the DELAY potentiometer with the ramp voltage of the main time base. This means, that the delay measured in *time* (s, ms, μs, or ns) is related to the MTB TIME/DIV setting. For this reason the DELAY potentiometer shown in Fig. 2.24 is inscribed DELAY TIME MULTIPLIER on the front panel of the oscilloscope. In order to have a precise multiplication factor, the DELAY potentiometer might be a 10-turn potentiometer with an accompanying scale from 00.0 to 10.0. If such a potentiometer is not provided, the delay time has to be determined from the screen.

Some important points to remember while operating the delayed time base are:

- The delayed time base can only operate if the main time base is running.

- Any portion of the input signal can be displayed and magnified as required, by varying the delay time and the delayed sweep speed.

- If the multiplier control is a 10-turn potentiometer, the start of the time window can be set accurately. Timing measurements can be made more accurately by operating the delayed time base than by the main time base alone.

• The amount of magnification is determined by the ratio of the TIME/DIV settings of the MTB and DTB. In this way, magnification factors of 1000 or more can be easily obtained.

2.14 MAIN TIME BASE INTENSIFIED AND ALTERNATE TIME BASE

As already stated in Sec. 2.12, excessive magnification makes it difficult to locate a particular part of the signal. With the delayed-time-base system this problem is solved by intensifying that part of the main-time-base sweep which is to be displayed by the delayed-time-base sweep. Figure 2.24 shows that both the MTB and the DTB systems produce an unblanking pulse. In Fig. 2.25 it can be seen how these unblanking pulses are added together and fed to the Wehnelt cylinder. The result on the screen is that the part of the signal to be studied with the aid of the DTB is further intensified. This will only be the case, however, if the *main sweep* is used for display. The intensified part is displayed (magnified) on the screen when switch Sk in Fig. 2.25 is in the delayed position.

Switch Sk in Fig. 2.25 may be replaced by an electronic switch, alternately connecting the main time base and the delayed time base to the horizontal deflection system. The electronic switch is activated at the end of each MTB sweep. The end of sweep information for the electronic switch is also used to shift both signals with respect to each other. This is accomplished by sequentially adding a small positive and negative voltage to the vertical amplifier system at the point where the POSITION is controlled (Fig. 2.25). When the switching is fast enough, the eye observes one steady display of two traces. In Fig. 2.26 the upper trace

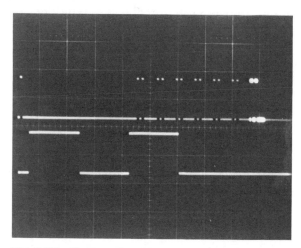

Fig. 2.26 Alternate time base facilitates the location of a particular part of the trace.

shows the signal as in the main-time-base intensified mode and the lower trace shows the signal as would normally be seen in the delayed-time-base mode. This feature facilitates observation of the location in the MAIN sweep the part of the signal which is to be studied in the DELAYED mode, together with the magnified picture at the same time. The alternate time-base facility is provided on only a relatively few types of oscilloscopes, such as the Philips PM 3265.

2.15 TRIGGERING THE DELAYED TIME BASE

Trigger Modes: STARTS and TRIG

As illustrated in Fig. 2.24, the delayed time base may start immediately after the main time base has reached the level at the DELAY potentiometer. But now the following may happen.

Assume that the signal to be tested is a pulse train and that the time between two successive pulses is not constant, but varies a little around the set repetition rate. The result will be a somewhat unstable display; this is known as *jitter*. The time between the first and the second pulses varies a little, as does the time between the second and the third pulses. The third pulse varies twice as much with respect to the first one as the second pulse does. The fourth pulse varies three times as much, and so on.

Operating the DTB in the STARTS mode now will show the jitter to be magnified to the same extent as the signal. In the STARTS mode the main time base is triggered at the first pulse, while the nth pulse is intensified after the delay time. In the DELAYED mode the nth pulse is displayed. As the variations are too quick for the eye to follow, the transitions of the pulses become a vague band. The width of the band is a measure of the jitter.

However, although the jitter can be measured, the shape of the nth pulse cannot be studied, because the display is too vague. But, by selecting the delayed-time-base trigger mode TRIG, the trigger pulse caused by the nth pulse will now start the delayed sweep, resulting in a stable display.

The timing diagram in Fig. 2.27 illustrates the operation of the delayed timebase in its TRIG and STARTS modes. In three successive cycles, the third pulse is seen to have jitter, which, for the purpose of explanation, is exaggerated. Figure 2.27*A* shows how a stable display is obtained in the TRIG mode. Figure 2.27*B* shows that in the STARTS mode pulse 3 varies in time and occupies the whole time window. It will be clear that pulse 3 cannot be studied now from the screen. Figure 2.28 shows a more realistic picture of jitter taken from the screen of an oscolloscope (Philips PM 3265) with alternate time-base facility.

Note: If the DELAY potentiometer is rotated in the STARTS trigger mode, the operator will notice the intensified part of the main time base shifting smoothly through the entire time window. In the TRIG mode, however, rotating the DELAY potentiometer will cause the intensified part to jump from one pulse to another, because the delayed time base is triggered each time by the first pulse after the DELAY time.

2.16 MIXED SWEEP

Another application of the second time base is for the display of "mixed sweep." Figure 2.29 gives two examples, both based on the same idea.

In the MAIN sweep position the display on the screen will be as shown in Fig. 2.29*A* and *E*. In the DEL'D position the display will be as shown in Fig. 2.29*B*.

When the switch is set to MIXED, the displays shown in Fig. 2.29*D* or *G* will appear. In this position the delayed time base is normally started with a delay predetermined by the setting of the DELAY control knob (as before, in Fig. 2.24). But in the case of Fig. 2.29*C*, the output of the delayed time base is compared with the sawtooth of the main sweep. As soon as the amplitude of the delayed sweep exceeds the instantaneous level of the main sweep, the deflection is electronically switched over to the former. Reference to Fig. 2.29*C* will make it clear that in this case a

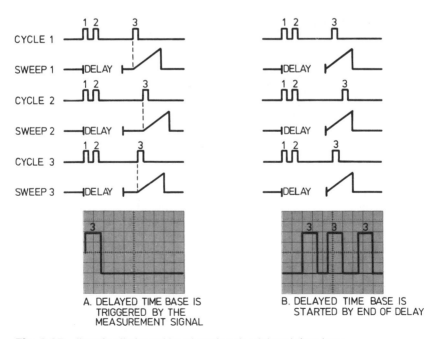

A. DELAYED TIME BASE IS
   TRIGGERED BY THE
   MEASUREMENT SIGNAL

B. DELAYED TIME BASE IS
   STARTED BY END OF DELAY

Fig. 2.27 Jitter is eliminated by triggering the delayed time base.

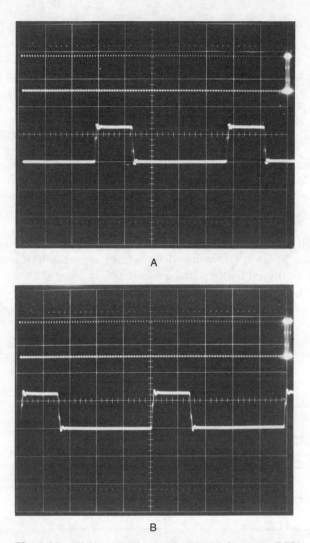

A

B

Fig. 2.28 (*A*) Alternate timebase, delayed time base (DTB) in STARTS mode shows jitter. (*B*) Alternate time base, delayed time base in TRIG mode gives a stable display. For *A* and *B*, upper trace MTB = 10 μs/div, lower trace DTB = 0.2 μs/div. The time magnification is 50 ×. The jitter is magnified 100 × because the 100th pulse approximately is intensified in the MTB on the right-hand side of the trace.

calibrated delay-time multiplier cannot be applied, because it takes some time after the delay before the amplitude of the delayed sweep will exceed that of the main sweep. Figure 2.29*F* shows an improvement over Fig. 2.29*C*. *At the moment* the delayed sweep becomes active, the sweep speed is taken over by it and is thus determined by its setting.

Mixed sweep is most valuable in digital applications where one pulse after the other can be observed and counted simply by varying the delay time. However, the alternate time-base mode is advantageous over the mixed-sweep mode in this case because the pulses can be counted equally well. Moreover, the whole MTB sweep is visible, indicating also the position (intensified) where we are counting.

2.17 DUAL-DELAYED TIME BASE

In Sec. 2.13 it is shown that the delayed time base is mainly used for:

1. Enlarging the time scale for the study of a particular part of the picture on the screen.

2. Performing more accurate time measurements with the aid of the calibrated 10-turn potentiometer by which the delay time is set.

A further utilization of the delayed-sweep facilities may lead to the measurement of an interval of time. For this purpose the dc input signal to the comparator in Fig. 2.24 may be derived from a circuit as is shown in Fig. 2.30.

The dc signal to which the MTB sawtooth voltage is compared comes from an electronic switch. After each MTB sweep this switch connects voltage A or B, alternating, to the comparator. The controlling voltage ALT may be derived from the SGM of the MTB (see Fig. 2.24).

When the switch is in position B, the situation is exactly the same as in Fig. 2.24, where the dc voltage is derived from the DELAY potentiometer.

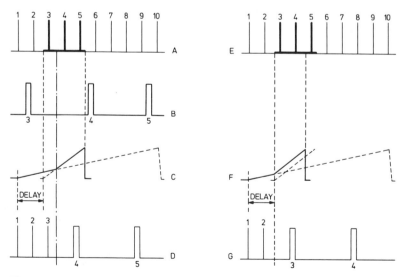

Fig. 2.29 Examples of mixed-sweep applications.

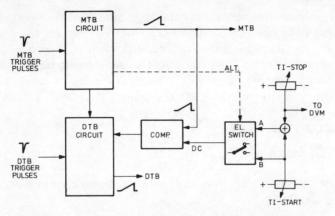

Fig. 2.30 Block diagram of a dual-delayed-time-base circuit.

In position A, a second dc voltage is added to the former. The DTB is now set ready slightly later than in position B.

Therefore, the potentiometer connected directly to input B of the electronic switch is labeled TI-START (start of the time interval) and the other one TI-STOP.

The first potentiometer may be a normal multiturn potentiometer; the second one possesses a calibrated scale. To increase the resolution of the measurement, the voltage at the slider of the TI-STOP potentiometer may be connccted to a built-in DVM.

In Fig. 2.31 an oscilloscope with a dual-delayed time base is shown. The digital readout of the measured time interval is positioned on top of the instrument. From the screen it can be seen that the TI-START movement (lower trace) coincides with the signal at input channel B. This can be set with a front-panel switch, depending on the operator's needs. Now, by adjusting the intensified parts of the MTB sweeps on those parts of the signals which are of interest, the difference in time can be read from the digital readout.

A more accurate and luxurious version of the dual-delayed time base, also available from Hewlett-Packard, is applied in their 1722A oscilloscope. Here, use is made of a microprocessor control to measure time intervals. Figure 2.32 shows the simplified block diagram. (The instrument may be seen in Fig. 3.49.)

The microprocessor generates the digital number on a LED display which represents the distance between the start movements of the two delayed sweeps (for example, the intensified parts at the screen in Fig. 2.31). This number is made larger or smaller through a DEC ↔ INC control (DECrease-INCrease). It is multiplied by the appropriate main-time-base setting for a direct reading at the LED display. This display, together with the DEC ↔ INC control, thus replaces the calibrated 10-turn potentiometer with or without the digital display, as in Fig. 2.31.

One can now ask: Why is a microprocessor used? First of all because it is a new technology, which is cheaper, especially in the microprocessor field. Once a microprocessor is applied, it can also compute the reciprocal of whatever was set into it. For example, in the TIME mode it can dis-

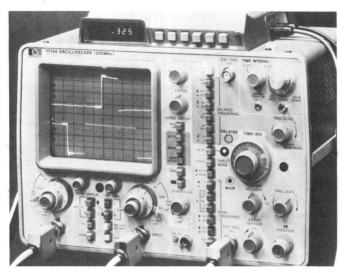

Fig. 2.31 Hewlett-Packard Model 1715A oscilloscope with direct readout for time-interval measurements. (*Photograph courtesy of Hewlett-Packard Benelux N.V.—Netherlands.*)

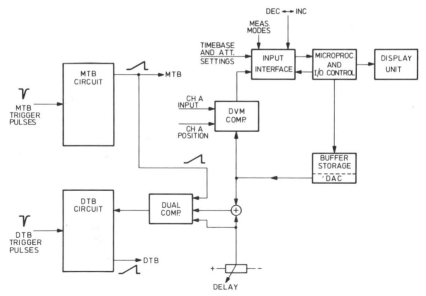

Fig. 2.32 Simplified block diagram of the HP 1722A's dual-delayed-time-base facility with microprocessor.

play the answer of 1/time (frequency). Or, by connecting a built-in DVM to the microprocessor, a signal's input voltage can be measured as well. In Fig. 2.32 (or Fig. 3.49) the latter applies to the signal at channel A for which the average voltage can be measured or the peak-to-peak value measured indirectly via the voltage at the slider of the VERT POSITION potentiometer.

2.18 EXERCISES

For each question, circle the answer you believe is correct.

1. Which trigger mode must be selected with low-repetition-rate signals ($F < 10$ Hz)?

   (A) AUTO mode

   (B) Normal trigger mode TRIG

   (C) Single sweep

2. When the Y POSITION control is varied, the start of the sweep remains at the same point in time on the waveform. This is because:

   (A) The dc component of the input signal is blocked.

   (B) The dc component of the trigger signal is blocked.

   (C) The internal trigger signal is picked off before the Y position control.

3.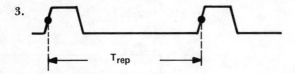

   The repetition time of this waveform varies considerably. Nonetheless, a stable display of this waveform can be obtained, provided that:

   (A) DC trigger coupling is selected.

   (B) The time window (10 × TIME/DIV) selected must be less than the minimum repetition time.

   (C) Both A and B.

4. A stable display of fast transition pulses cannot be obtained with the trigger-coupling switch in the lf position, because:

   (A) Fast pulses to the trigger circuitry are attenuated or integrated.

   (B) Chopping frequencies may interfere with the triggering.

   (C) Charging and discharging of the trigger input capacitor occurs.

5. Sophisticated oscilloscopes are equipped with a delay line in the vertical channel to:

   (A) Correct for phase shifts in the horizontal channel

   (B) Bring the complete trigger transition on screen

   (C) Allow faster sweep speeds

6. With pulse patterns on both channels of a dual-trace oscilloscope in the alternate mode, an untrue time shift may occur. This can be verified by:

   (A) Switching to the chopped mode

   (B) Resetting the LEVEL control

   (C) Changing the VAR HOLD OFF control

7. With a dual-beam oscilloscope a stable display of two nonrelated signals can be obtained. This statement is:

   (A) True.

   (B) Only true if the COMP (composite triggering) switch is depressed.

   (C) Not true, because no electronic switch is used.

8. Which of the following statements is true?

   (A) With ac coupling, signals riding on a large dc level cannot be positioned on screen at high sensitivity.

   (B) With ac coupling, distortion on low-repetition-rate signals occurs.

   (C) With ac coupling at the Y input, and internal triggering. dc trigger coupling cannot be used beneficially.

9. In normal delayed-time-base operation (STARTS), the delayed time base is started by:

   (A) End of the main sweep

   (B) End of the delay time

   (C) Depends on the TIME/DIV setting of the delayed time base

10. Delay time is dependent upon:

    (A) MTB TIME/DIV setting only

    (B) DTB TIME/DIV and MULTIPLIER settings

    (C) MTB TIME/DIV and MULTIPLIER settings

11. A triggered delayed time base (DTB trigger switch in the TRIG position) is mainly intended:

(A) To eliminate jitter

(B) To make jitter measurements

(C) To obtain better accuracy of timing measurements

12. In delayed-time-base operation the time axis is:

(A) Not calibrated

(B) Calibrated by the delayed-time-base TIME/DIV setting

(C) Calibrated by the main-time-base TIME/DIV setting

13. With the main-time-base trigger-mode switch in the normal TRIG position, and the delayed-time-base trigger switch in the STARTS position,

(A) The delayed sweep cannot run.

(B) Delayed sweep can only run with an external trigger signal applied to the DTB circuit.

(C) As B, provided that the main-time-base trigger controls (LEVEL, SLOPE, and TRIGGER SOURCE) are appropriately set and a signal is present.

SPECIAL OSCILLOSCOPES
AND VARIANTS

3.1 THE STORAGE OSCILLOSCOPE

Storage Principles

Storage oscilloscopes are used in those applications where the display time at the screen is too short to examine the signals to be measured. If a single-shot signal is to be measured, only one sweep is generated. During this sweep the screen is excited by the high-energy electron beam (see Chap. 1). When the beam is suppressed at the end of the single sweep, a phosphorescence remains for some time. The time that the phosphorescence remains visible is dependent upon the type of phosphor used and is referred to as the *persistence* of the tube. The persistence is the time that the intensity, after the excitation, takes to decay to a level of $1/e$ of the level attained during excitation ($e \approx 2.72$ = base of natural logarithms). Table 3.1 shows the persistence times for various types of phosphor as used in the manufacture of oscilloscope cathode-ray tubes.

A storage CRT can extend the persistence time in excess of minutes. The storage principle is based upon the phenomenon of secondary emission. Furthermore, for the storage layer a composition is used which possesses not only *good secondary emission* but also *good isolation* against cross-migration of electric charge of the particles loaded by secondary emission. Various compositions may be used, such as:

- Silicon sulfide
- Barium fluoride
- Magnesium fluoride
- Magnesium oxide

When the electron beam of the CRT hits the layer of particles of the composition with the high energy caused by the acceleration voltage, more secondary electrons are emitted from the particles than are captured from the primary electrons that have hit them. Thus, the bombarded particles become positively charged. Due to the insulation property, the pattern written by the high-energy beam remains as a charge pattern at the layer. This charge pattern is later used to visualize the pat-

Table 3.1

Type of phosphor	Persistence time, ms
P_7	60
P_{11}	20
P_{31}	0.6

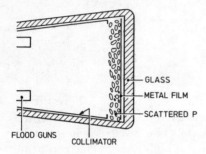

GLASS
METAL FILM
SCATTERED P
FLOOD GUNS
COLLIMATOR

Fig. 3.1 The construction of the bistable storage cathode-ray tube.

tern again. For this purpose special techniques have been developed for storage CRTs. The two techniques most commonly used are discussed in the following paragraphs, as well as the advantages and disadvantages of each technique.

The Bistable Cathode-Ray Tube

The first commercially available storage CRT was the bistable cathode-ray tube (Tektronix). Here the phosphor used for the screen is applied in scattered particles in order to avoid cross-migration of the stored charge (see Fig. 3.1). The layer of scattered phosphor may be more than one particle thick to give a homogeneous display on the screen.

Before the phosphor is deposited on the screen, a transparent metal film is first deposited on the inside surface. This conductive layer acts as a controlling electrode. The writing beam—the focused high-energy beam of the CRT electron gun—hits the particles with such an energy that a charge pattern is caused, as already described. In order to visualize this pattern again after writing, a cloud of low-energy electrons is sent towards the screen from a pair of *flood guns* in the CRT. The shape and speed of this low-energy cloud is controlled by the voltage of the transparent metal layer. On those parts of the screen where the particles have a positive charge, the energy of the flood-gun electrons is sufficient to illuminate the phosphor. On all the other parts of the screen, the low-energy electrons do not have enough energy to illuminate the phosphor. They are repelled and have to be collected by the metal film in the cone of the tube collimator. In this way a replica of the formerly written waveform is achieved. This type of storage CRT is said to be of a bistable nature; that is, no halftones are possible.

A particular advantage of this system is the ability to split up the metal film backplate into upper and lower halves. Therefore, for comparison purposes a waveform can be stored in the upper half of the screen, while the lower half can be used in the normal mode for the operator's measurements.

Construction of the Variable-Persistence Tube

A second type of storage tube is the mesh storage tube, which makes use of a dielectric material deposited on a storage mesh as a target. The mesh is located between the deflection plates and the normal standard phosphor screen of the CRT, about 6 mm in front of the screen when viewed from the deflection plates.

The mesh storage tube works on much the same principle as the bistable tube. Positively charged areas of the storage target allow electrons from the flood guns to pass through the mesh towards the standard phosphor, thereby reproducing the stored replica. As this type of storage tube is the most widely used, its construction is described in somewhat more detail.

Figure 3.2 shows that the storage CRT contains two systems: the writing system and the flood system. The construction and operation of the writing system is identical to that of a conventional CRT and need not be further explained. The flood system consists of a pair of flood guns operated in parallel, both having a cathode k, a control grid g_1, and an accelerator grid g_2. Common to both flood guns are the flood-beam collimator g_7, the collector mesh g_8, the *storage mesh* g_9 carrying the *storage*

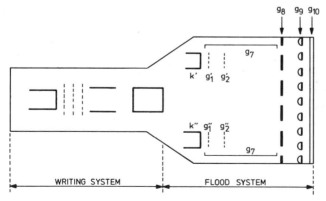

Fig. 3.2 Simplified construction of a variable-persistence storage cathode-ray tube.

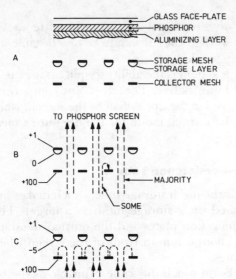

Fig. 3.3 (A) Details of storage system construction. (B) Storage system at full brightness. (C) Storage system at cut-off.

layer, and the phosphor viewing screen g_{10} with its aluminized layer (see also Fig. 3.3A).

The flood guns are located just outside the horizontal deflection plates. A cloud of electrons is emitted by each flood-gun cathode. These clouds are combined, shaped, and accelerated by the two control grids, g_1 and g_2, and by the collimator g_7. The collimator consists of a coating on the inside of the tube. The positive voltage on the collimator is adjusted such that the flood-gun electron cloud just fills the CRT viewing screen. The cloud is further accelerated towards the storage mesh and viewing screen by the collector mesh g_8. After passing through the collector mesh, the flood electrons are further controlled by the potentials of the storage mesh and storage layer. The cathode side of the storage mesh is coated with the nonconductive storage material, as previously described in Sec. 3.1, under Storage Principles. It is here the pattern to be displayed is stored (Fig. 3.3). Because of the nonconductive property, only a capacitive coupling exists between the storage layer and the storage mesh. This capacitive coupling is essential for the storage and erase functions. The rest potential of the storage *mesh* is approximately + 1 V with respect to the flood-gun cathodes. In the write and erase routines the potential of the storage *layer* varies from 0 V to negative. This is accomplished via the storage mesh and the capacitive coupling.

Figure 3.3B shows that when the storage-layer surface is at 0 V, the majority of the flood electrons pass through the holes of the mesh and reach the viewing screen. The remaining electrons are repelled by the storage-layer surface and picked up by the collector mesh. The postaccelerator voltage (approximately 6 kV with respect to the storage mesh) is connected to the transparent aluminizing layer of the phosphor viewing screen. As soon as flood electrons are allowed to pass the storage mesh, they are accelerated by the high potential and strike the phosphor, causing it to emit light. When the storage layer is made negative (Fig. 3.3*C*), the number of electrons passing the storage mesh is reduced considerably. At a certain value—the cutoff level—no electrons are passed.

Operating the Variable-Persistence Tube

Write and Store Modes

Assume that the storage-layer surface has been prepared by an erase routine (to be discussed later) such that the layer is below the cutoff level and no flood electrons can reach the screen (Fig. 3.3*C*). The writing cathode is activated and the beam writes in one sweep the pattern at the storage layer. The writing cathode is at about -1500-V potential with respect to the storage layer, which is sufficient to cause the secondary emission. During the writing procedure, the highest potential of the storage layer that can be reached is 0 V (flood-gun cathode potential), because any higher potential would attract flood-gun electrons, thereby reducing this potential. After writing, with the storage layer at 0 V, the majority of the flood-gun electrons can pass through the mesh (Fig. 3.3*B*). Thus the pattern of charge on the storage layer is made visible on the screen.

The brightness of the displayed pattern, as it is stored on the storage layer, can be varied by applying a pulse-shaped waveform to the accelerator grid g_2. The amplitudes of the pulses are $+50$ V with respect to the flood-gun cathode and the storage brightness has a linear relationship with the pulse *width*. For full brightness the pulse width is at maximum, and when the pulse width is at minimum, the brightness is also at minimum, but now the storage *time* is at maximum (see Fig. 3.4), Figure 3.5 summarizes the operation of the write and store modes.

At this point it must be understood that the structure of the storage mesh is very fine, about 240 lines/cm, to ensure a bright and crisp display. As the focused writing beam has a spot diameter of about 0.3 mm, one trace covers about 7 to 8 mesh lines.

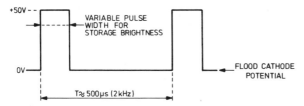

Fig. 3.4 Control voltage at accelerator grid g_2 for storage brightness.

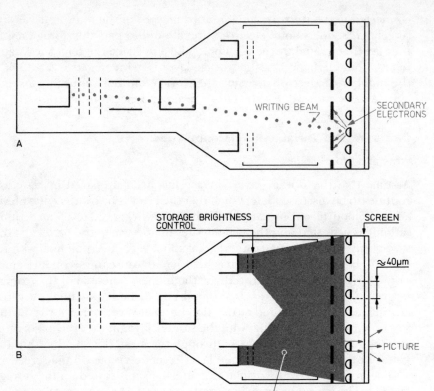

Fig. 3.5 Storing and displaying a picture. (*A*) The picture is written by the writing beam. (*B*) The picture is displayed on the screen by means of the flood electrons.

Variable-Persistence Mode

Thus far the method of storing and displaying a single sweep pattern has been discussed. Although *this* application of the storage oscilloscope is the best-known, the variable-persistence mode also facilitates very well the study of extreme low-frequency signals. In an ordinary oscilloscope such signals would result in a flickering display or even merely a moving spot on the screen, in which case no history of the signal could be studied.

In the variable-persistence mode the spot is given a tail and the display on the screen can be compared with the trace of a meteor in the dark sky. Now some history of the signal can be studied from the screen. To obtain such a picture, the accelerator grids g_2 are brought to a $+50$-V level with respect to the flood-gun cathode and a pulsed voltage of 10-V amplitude and variable (controllable) width is applied to the storage *mesh* (see Fig. 3.6*A*).

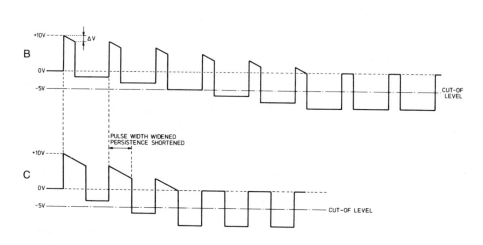

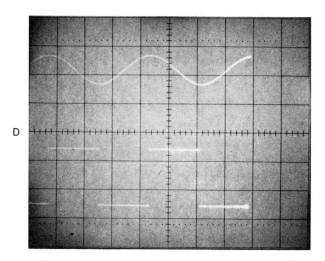

Fig. 3.6 Voltages at the storage layer in the variable persistence mode. (*A*) Voltage at the storage mesh. (*B*) Voltage at the storage layer; after the decay of the written pattern the pulses are clamped to OV. A little background light remains. (*C*) With wider pulses, less pulses are needed for the decay of the written pattern and more background light is visible. (*D*) The tail of slow moving spots provides some history in a light background (see photograph).

Owing to the $+50$ V, at g_2 all flood-gun electrons flow towards the storage layer, and while the writing beam is still moving slowly, flood-gun electrons arrive at the layer also. Because of the capacitive coupling, together with the mesh, the storage *layer* is also instantaneously raised by 10 V, to a level of $+10$ V above its 0-V level, which was the maximum during writing. Now, during each pulse, the layer becomes positive, and it will attract and capture flood-gun electrons which lower its potential slightly to ΔV (Fig. 3.6B).

If this procedure is frequently repeated, enough electrons will be captured to compensate for the secondary-emission electrons from the writing procedure. At this point the stored pattern (the history) has disappeared. No further flood-gun electrons will be captured during the pulses, because this would lead to a negative voltage of the layer (with respect to the flood-gun cathode), which repels electrons. Thus, after the decay of the written pattern, the pulses are clamped to 0 V (Fig. 3.6B), which was the case for all other places on the screen outside the pattern area.

It must be understood that the pulses are applied to the storage mesh and that they influence the behavior of the entire storage layer. During the pulses the majority of the flood-gun electrons can pass toward the screen (see Fig. 3.3B). This results in some light over the whole screen, the amount of which is dependent upon the duty cycle of the pulses. This is known as "background light."

When the duty cycle of the pulses is increased (increased pulse width), fewer pulses are needed for the decay of the written pattern (shorter history) and the background light will increase (see Fig. 3.6C). In this way the persistence is varied, that is, adjusted by means of a front-panel control knob. The persistence can be varied between 0.3 and 10 min.

Erasure

The ERASE mode serves two purposes: to erase the stored pattern, and to prepare the storage layer for a new writing procedure. In the ERASE mode the potential at the storage mesh is varied according to the curve shown in Fig. 3.7A. The corresponding curve for the storage-layer potential is shown in Fig. 3.7B. When the ERASE push button is depressed, and held (t_1), the storage mesh is changed to the same potential as the collector mesh ($+100$ V). Because of the capacitive coupling, the storage-layer surface changes also—to almost the same potential. Since this surface is being bombarded by flood-gun electrons now having an energy of 100 eV, secondary emission will take place equally spread over the whole surface. As a result the entire *storage layer* becomes even more positive, exceeding $+100$ V. The excess is not much beyond this level, because then the *collector* mesh becomes negative with respect to the layer, thereby repeling the secondary electrons. This again tends to decrease the potential at the layer.

When the ERASE pushbutton is released (t_2), the storage mesh returns to $+1$ V and the storage layer drops by the same amount, due to the capacitive coupling. Although the layer is a positive level, it captures flood-gun electrons and its potential decays to 0 V (see Fig. 3.7B). Now the stored pattern is erased.

After 200 ms (t_3), the storage mesh is automatically raised to $+11$ V, where it is maintained for 400 ms. The storage-layer surface rises to $+10$ V by means of the capacitive coupling, but immediately starts decaying towards 0 V by capturing flood-gun electrons. At the end of the 400 ms (t_4), the storage mesh is brought back to $+1$ V. This reduces the storage layer surface from 0 to -10 V. The second erasure cycle is now completed also, and the system is ready for a new writing procedure.

Maximum Write Mode

When the MAX WRITE pushbutton is depressed, the ERASE system responds in much the same way as in the normal mode in which the rest level of the *storage layer* is -10 V. The storage threshold level (cutoff level) is still about -5 V. By depressing the MAX WRITE pushbutton, the rest level of the storage layer is brought to about this -5-V level by reducing the 400-ms storage mesh pulse, shown in Fig. 3.7A, by approximately half (see Fig. 3.8A).

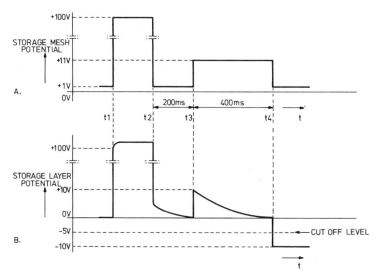

Fig. 3.7 Applied voltages in the ERASE mode. (*A*) Storage mesh potential during erase cycle. (*B*) Storage layer potential during erase cycle.

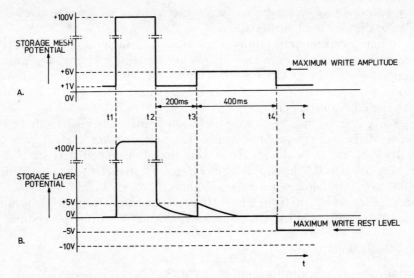

Fig. 3.8 Applied voltages in the MAX WRITE mode. (*A*) Storage mesh potential during maximum write cycle. (*B*) Storage layer potential during maximum write cycle.

With the rest level already at − 5 V, a weaker positive-charge pattern is required to allow the flood-gun electrons to pass; hence, fewer writing-gun electrons are required to obtain this charge pattern in the storage layer. Consequently, the writing beam may move faster (fewer writing electrons per unit of time at the same spot), which means an increase in writing speed. At the same time, however, some of the flood-gun electrons are also permitted to pass the storage layer toward the screen, at the noncharged places. This results in the background brightening slightly, reducing the contrast of the pattern. However, the writing speed for fast single-shot signals is increased between 10 and 20 times.

Normal Mode

The storage CRT can be used as a normal CRT, in which case the accelerator grid g_2 (Fig. 3.2) is at a constant level (+ 50 V) and the *storage mesh* is at flood-cathode level (0 V or grounded). The slow flood-gun electrons cannot pass the storage layer and are collected by the collector mesh g_8, which remains at + 100 V. The fast-writing-speed electrons, however, which can pass the collector mesh and the storage layer, are accelerated again by the 6-kV postaccelerator voltage at the aluminized layer, and a normal picture is obtained on the screen.

Warning: Care should be taken to operate the oscilloscope in the variable-persistence mode whenever possible, as the storage layer may become damaged by too high amounts of high-energy electrons if the intensity control is set for intensities which are usual in normal CRTs. This would be visible in the storage mode by a blooming trace.

Erasure with the Writing Beam

While operating the storage oscilloscope, a picture could possibly be written with much too high an intensity. As already mentioned this can also be the situation with the storage layer in the NORMAL MODE. In such an event, too many secondary electrons are emitted and the ERASE procedure is unable to restore the layer. The damage caused to the layer can be demonstrated in the variable-persistence mode with the shortest persistence time (wide pulses, Fig. 3.6C). The background is then illuminated over the whole screen, but in the places where the storage layer is damaged, the background remains slightly darker.

Another method of trying to erase the layer is to strike the entire storage-layer surface with the high-speed writing electrons. The oscilloscope should be set up as follows:

- Set the storage to VARIABLE PERSISTENCE, with the shortest persistence.

- Set the time-base trigger to AUTO.

- Adjust the vertical POSITION such that there is only one trace mid scale.

- Select the lowest possible setting of the TIME/DIV switch, for example, 0.5 s/div.

- Apply a sine-wave signal of relatively high frequency to the input, for example, 10 kHz.

- Set the vertical AMPLITUDE for several screen heights, for example, 1-V peak-to-peak signal at 50 mV/div.

A vertical trace with a short tail should be visible against a light background. The trace should move slowly over the screen from left to right. The damaged areas (dark) are also visible but may possibly disappear after a *couple of hours*. The effect is demonstrated in Fig. 3.9A and B. It should be noted that this method of erasing is a rough treatment for the storage layer because there is no remedy that can restore the layer where it has been completely burned in.

The Charge-Transfer Storage Cathode-Ray Tube

Apart from the bistable and the variable-persistence tubes, the most recent tube development today is the charge-transfer storage tube. This system incorporates an extra mesh to the storage system of the variable-persistence cathode-ray tube (see Fig. 3.10). Section 3.1, under Storage

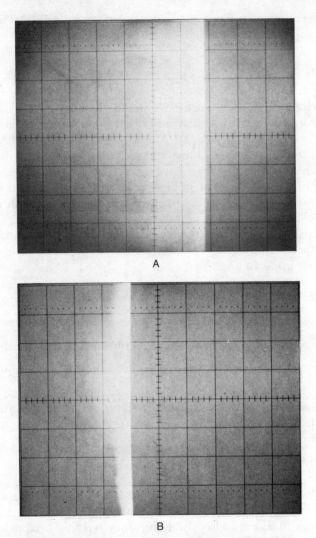

Fig. 3.9 A vertical trace having a short tail moving from left to right across the screen is visible against a light background. (A) The burned-in pattern is still visible. (B) The storage layer is cleared by the writing beam after a couple of hours.

Principles, explained that the storage material must possess two properties: good secondary emission, and good isolation against cross-migration of electrons. In the transfer storage tube the pattern is written on the first mesh (as viewed from the flood gun), which is optimized for good secondary emission. The pattern at the mesh can only be stored for a few seconds. Therefore, as soon as the storage pattern is written, it is transferred to the second mesh, which is optimized for good insulation and, consequently, for good storage.

To accomplish the transfer, use is made of the flood-gun electrons, which are present as a cloud but are unable to reach the screen. After the single sweep a short pulse-shaped voltage of very high amplitude (about 600 V) is routinely fed to the second storage mesh. At those places where the pattern was written at the first mesh, the high pulse voltage can reach through and attract, and capture, flood-gun electrons with sufficient energy to store the pattern. From this point onward the normal routines in the variable-persistence CRT are used to display the pattern at the screen.

Because subsequent use is made of the two material properties, both optimized, the transfer-storage CRT can achieve writing speeds three to four times faster than those of the fastest variable-persistence CRT. A typical speed is 1300 to 1400 cm/μs.

Measuring the Writing Speed of a Storage Cathode-Ray Tube

As the writing speed of a storage tube is defined rather precisely, the measuring procedure is described here in detail.

From the specifications of the storage tube it may follow that the writing speed is not defined over the entire surface of the screen but only over a certain area. The area for the tube used in a Philips PM 3243 oscilloscope is shown in Fig. 3.11.

A writing speed may be given as 0.2 div/μs in a single-shot mode. The INTENSITY of the beam should be set to maximum and the focus optimized. The writing speed can be checked easily by means of a triangular waveform from a function generator. The procedure is to control the amplitude per division of the oscilloscope, and the amplitude setting of the generator, such that a triangular voltage of 24 divisions is obtained,

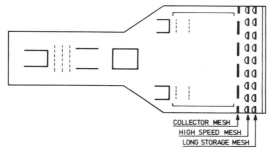

Fig. 3.10 Construction of the transfer-storage cathode-ray tube.

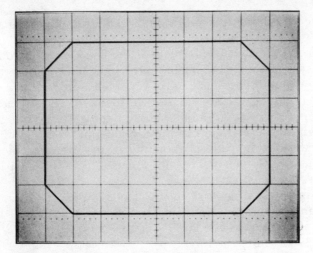

Fig. 3.11 The writing speed is defined and specified within a certain area of a storage cathode-ray tube. This illustration shows the area of the tube in a Philips PM 3243 oscilloscope.

or 3 screen heights, (= dynamic range, see Sec 5.1). The VERT POSITION must be centered at the horizontal center axis of the screen.

Observing these requirements, 8 vertical screen divisions should be written in 40 μs (8/0.2). The display on the screen is one third of a half period; thus the period time of the triangular voltage must be 240 μs (6 × 40). The frequency is then 4.2 kHz approximately.

A 5-kHz triangular waveform is illustrated in Fig. 3.12. If the TIME/DIV switch is set to 1 ms, then 5 periods per division, or 10 traces per division, are displayed on the screen. The photograph clearly shows the lack of intensity in the corners of the screen. However, compared with the defined area in Fig. 3.11, it can be seen that the tube used in Fig. 3.12 is well within its specification.

3.2 THE SAMPLING OSCILLOSCOPE

What is Sampling?

Sampling is the taking of a specimen, or a part, to illustrate the whole. When, for example, a ship's cargo of sugar has to be checked for the amount (%) of water in the sugar, specimens of the sugar are taken from different places in the ship. The more specimens taken, the more information is available about the quality of the cargo as a whole. It is evident that to be 100% sure about the condition of the cargo, all the sugar present in the ship would have to be checked; for obvious reasons this is not possible.

The same is applicable in oscilloscopy. For several reasons it is hardly possible to display directly a very high frequency (vhf) signal (say, above 1000 MHz) on the CRT of a normal real-time oscilloscope. However, by means of sampling techniques, it is possible to display frequencies of over 10,000 MHz. As with the specimens of the ship's cargo, samples of the vhf signal waveform can be taken and examined on the CRT. The more samples taken at different places on the signal waveform, the more information can be obtained about the shape of the signal.

Figure 3.13 illustrates the sampling idea. In Fig. 3.13*A* only a few samples are taken of a signal, and merely a couple of dotted lines are visible on the screen. In Fig. 3.13*B* more samples are taken and it becomes apparent that the signal waveform is pulse-shaped. In Fig. 3.13*C* so many samples of the signal are taken that not only is one sure about the pulse waveform, but also the pulse aberrations can be studied from the screen.

In the case of taking samples of the ship's sugar cargo, it goes without saying that the cargo is at hand every time a sample has to be taken. The same applies for the sampling oscilloscope too; the signal must be present every time a sample is taken.

This is where the analogy with the ship's cargo ends, because with the sampling oscilloscope the samples can only be taken sequentially in time. This means that for every sample the next signal waveform must be

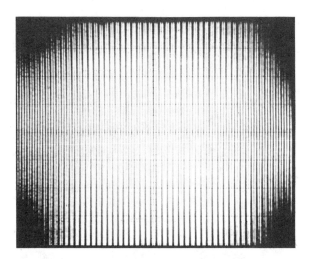

Fig. 3.12 This 5-kHz triangular waveform of 3 screen heights amplitude is displayed in the single-shot mode. The result is well within specifications (compare carefully with the defined area in Fig. 3.11).

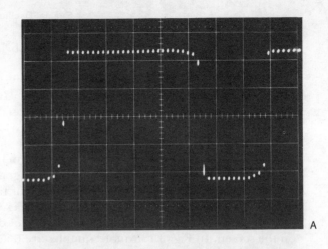

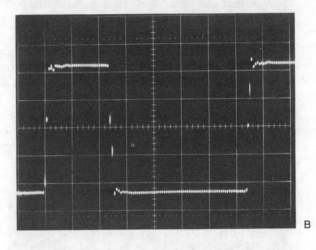

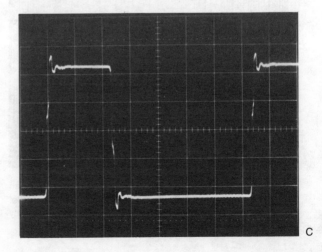

present. In other words the signal waveform must be repetitive (not necessarily periodic), and this again means that single-shot phenomena can never be displayed on a sampling oscilloscope, which is a drawback.

Often the sampling rate is low with respect to the rate of the signal waveform, so that a sample is taken only every now and then on a waveform of the signal. For example, a sample may be taken of the 1st, 101st, 201st, and 301st waveforms. As a matter of fact, only the input circuits, sampling gates, and trigger inputs must be able to handle vhf signals. Once the samples are taken and stored, all further electronic circuits in the sampling oscilloscope can be, and often are, relatively low-frequency circuits.

However, it obviously does not matter to the operator in which way the signal is displayed on the CRT, provided it can be studied on the screen. But, due to different setups, the sampling oscilloscope offers possibilities to the user which are hard to achieve with normal, real-time oscilloscopes. Consequently, the introduction of the sampling oscilloscope has led to new applications of oscilloscopy in general. Before discussing new applications, it is first necessary to know and to understand the setup of sampling systems.

This will make the operator more conversant with the oscilloscope and give him or her a better understanding of the results on the screen.

Random Sampling versus Sequential Sampling

Today, the two sampling techniques most commonly applied are random sampling and sequential sampling.

In the *random-sampling* technique no time relation exists between the timing-ramp voltage (trigger-source functioning) and the sampling instant. Owing to this, the picture on the screen is built up with samples which appear at places scattered at random over the waveform. In the *sequential-sampling* technique, which is the technique most frequently employed, the successive samples appear on the screen at adjacent places over the waveform because a comparison circuit links the sampling instants to the timing ramp voltages when triggered by the imput signal.

A better understanding of the random-sampling technique will be obtained by referring to Figs. 3.14 and 3.15. During each sample, switch S_1 (Fig. 3.15) is closed and the instantaneous amplitude is stored in the Y memory for display on the screen. The sampling pulse is delayed by a

Fig. 3.13 Illustration of the sampling idea. (*A*) Only a few samples of the waveform have been taken. Mainly two dotted lines are visible, suggesting a pulse waveform is displayed. (*B*) More samples reveal the waveform in greater detail. (*C*) Enough samples are taken to display all the details of the pulse waveform, including the aberrations.

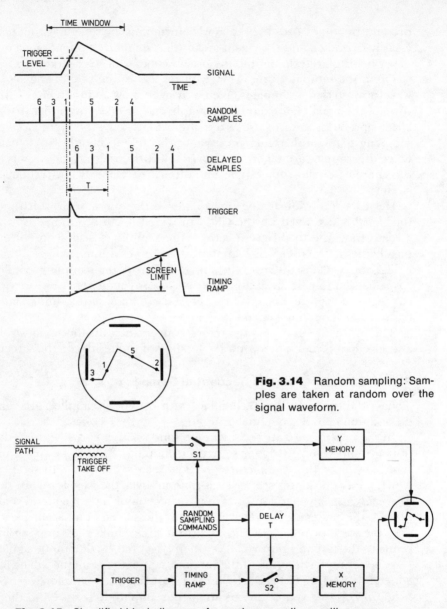

Fig. 3.14 Random sampling: Samples are taken at random over the signal waveform.

Fig. 3.15 Simplified block diagram of a random-sampling oscilloscope.

fixed time interval T. This delayed sampling pulse is used to sample the timing ramp which was started by a trigger signal taken from the signal. The resulting sample is stored in the X memory for display on the screen. As can be seen from Fig. 3.15, the time delay T is necessary to display the leading edge of a transient on the screen also.

A disadvantage of this system is that a high trigger repetition rate is required to obtain an adequate picture of the signal. A CRT screen with a somewhat higher persistence can partly overcome this disadvantage.

Sequential sampling is taking samples of the signal one after the other, again on successive repetitions of the signal. Care must be taken to set up the oscilloscope correctly before proceeding with sequential sampling (Figs. 3.16 and 3.17).

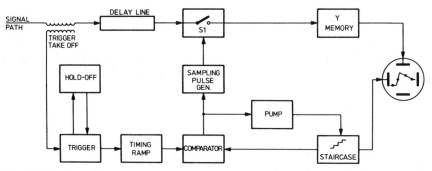

Fig. 3.16 Simplified block diagram of a sequential-sampling oscilloscope.

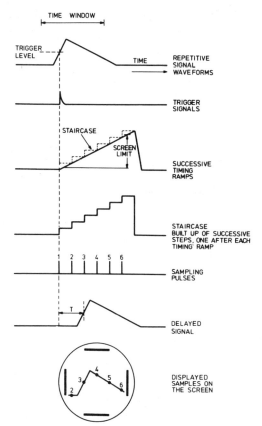

Fig. 3.17 Sequential sampling: Samples are displayed adjacent to each other along the waveform.

After each hold-off period a successive trigger pulse starts the timing-ramp generator. The comparator compares the ramp voltage with the output of the staircase generator, which also delivers the horizontal deflection voltage. When the ramp voltage equals the staircase voltage, the comparator delivers a pulse to the sampling pulse generator and to the pump generator.

The sampling pulse opens the sampling gate S_1, and a sample of the delayed input voltage is taken and fed to the Y memory for the vertical deflection at the CRT. The pump generator initiates the staircase generator to the next higher step, so that the next sample will be displayed next to the former one. In this way the samples taken from the input signal are displayed in a sequential order from left to right on the screen.

It is obvious that the input signal has to pass a delay line before the sampling gate S_1 if the complete leading edge of an input signal is to be displayed. Otherwise, just as in the real-time oscilloscope, the finite trigger level to be reached to derive a trigger pulse, added to the propagation delays in the time-base and trigger circuits, would prevent this happening. Refer to Fig. 3.17 and also compare with the details given in Sec. 2.5.

However, the implementation of the delay line is a disadvantage, because it must pass the full bandwidth. This may lead again to bandwidth limitations and inherent distortions. Nevertheless, the advantages of this method in practice outweigh the advantage of the random-sampling method. But in both methods the advantages of sampling are clearly seen. Only the sampling circuits of the oscilloscope have to operate at the very high speeds required for the vhf signal to be measured, while the rest of the oscilloscope circuits are relatively low-frequency ones.

Some Details of a Sampling Oscilloscope

To understand the advantages of the sampling technique, a more detailed description of the structure and the function of a sequential-sampling oscilloscope is given, using a Philips PM3400 oscilloscope. This instrument is a dual-trace oscilloscope with two identical vertical channels. One channel and the time base are described in the following paragraphs. A block diagram (Fig. 3.22) will complete the description.

Vertical Channel

A simplified diagram of the sampling bridge network and the position amplifier is illustrated in Fig. 3.18.

The signal is fed to the input channel of the oscilloscope by means of the low-impedance (50 Ω) Y IN socket. Part of the signal is taken off by the trigger take-off transformer which feeds the trigger circuitry. This will be described in detail later in this chapter. The signal passes through a delay line, the function of which has already been described.

From the delay line the signal enters the sampling bridge, consisting of diodes D, resistors R_1, and two windings of transformer Tr. Usually, the diodes D are reverse-biased via resistors R_3. Potentiometer R_4 controls the quiescent bias of the diodes and also the rise time of the oscilloscope.

Diodes D are opened by the sampling pulses (200 ps) from the sampling pulse generator via capacitors C_1. Depending upon the signal at a certain sampling instant with respect to the previous sampling instant, the bridge will be either balanced (no output signal) or unbalanced (output signal). In the latter case, a signal is induced in transformer Tr and passed to the memory through C_2 and the ac amplifier. A feedback voltage from the memory output is applied to the bridge at the junction of resistors R_1 via the feedback attenuator. As the bridge is floating, the feedback voltage will change the potential of the whole bridge, causing the reverse bias of the sampling diodes to change.

Example: The signal shown in Fig. 3.19 is applied to the sampling gate. In the quiescent state, the reverse bias of the sampling diodes is $+3$ V and -3 V, respectively. At sampling instant 1 the input voltage level is 0 V and the feedback voltage from the memory should also be 0 V. At sampling instant 2, the input level is -1 V, but the feedback voltage is still 0 V. This means that, seen from the sampling gate, the bridge is un-

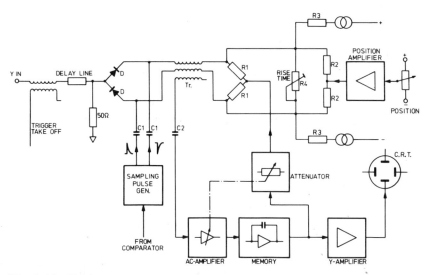

Fig. 3.18 Block diagram of the vertical channel of a sequential-sampling oscilloscope, including the sampling bridge.

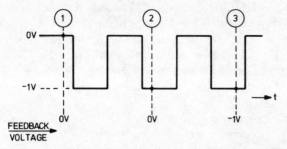

Fig. 3.19 Feedback voltages to the sampling bridge (Fig. 3.18) respond to changes in the signal level.

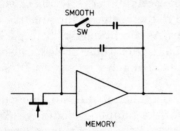

Fig. 3.20 The smoothing circuit.

balanced. A change proportional to the difference in level at sampling instants 1 and 2 will be fed to the memory from the third winding of transformer Tr through C_2 and the ac amplifier. At sampling instant 3, the input level is the same as at instant 2. The feedback voltage, however, has changed to -1 V, thus changing the bias of the diodes to $+2$ V and -4 V, respectively. Now, at instant 3, seen from the sampling gate, the bridge is balanced and no signal is applied to the ac amplifier. Thus the output voltage of the memory remains the same, as it should be, in fact.

By changing the potential of the whole bridge, the trace can be shifted vertically on the CRT screen. This is achieved by the POSITION potentiometer via the position amplifier, which in turn feeds the node of resistors R_2.

Loop Gain and Smoothing

To ensure good operation, the loop gain of the signal path through transformer Tr, the ac amplifier, the memory, and the feedback attenuator must be unity. When the loop gain is less than unity, more samples are required to ensure a correct reproduction of the input waveform. For example, with only a few samples per centimeter, the shoulder of a displayed square-wave signal is likely to be rounded.

However, this allows the signal-to-noise ratio to be improved. When a signal has a noise content, and when a reduction in loop gain makes more samples necessary to reproduce the input waveform, the noise will be averaged out at the memory capacitor. The reduction in loop gain is easy to obtain (see Fig. 3.20). By closing the electronic switch *Sw,* the feedback capacitance of the integrator is increased, requiring more samples to reach the same output voltage. In this way a *smoothed* picture is the result. It must be borne in mind that the horizontal steps of the successive samples on the screen must be set to a maximum per division. With the PM 3400 oscilloscope it is possible to have over 1000 samples per centimeter. In this case an integration over 30 samples gives a horizontal deflection of 0.3 mm on the screen, which equals one spot diameter. To prevent influencing the loop gain at the various settings of the input attenuator (part of the ac amplifier), the feedback attenuator is mechanically coupled to the former.

Time-Base Controls and Their Function

The time-base controls of the PM 3400 oscilloscope can be explained most satisfactorily if reference is made to Fig. 3.21. Part of the vertical input signal is taken off by the trigger take-off transformer and supplied to the trigger circuit. This circuit can also accept trigger signals from an

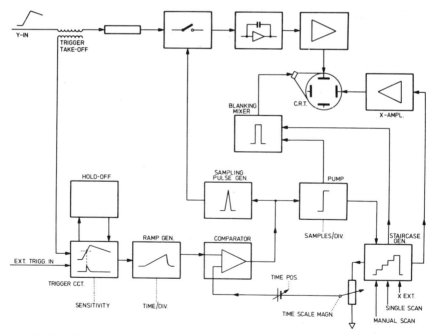

Fig. 3.21 Block diagram of the horizontal channel of a sequential-sampling oscilloscope.

external source (EXT TRIG IN). The pulses from the trigger start a ramp generator. The slope of the ramp generator is determined by the position of the TIME/DIV switch. In the comparator stage this ramp voltage is compared to a voltage derived from the staircase generator. When the ramp voltage equals the staircase voltage, the comparator supplies a strobe pulse which is fed to the sampling pulse generator and to the pump circuit. Here it must be noted that the maximum voltage reached by the staircase generator remains constant and thus independent of any setting of the controls. This maximum voltage is matched to fit the screen width.

The number of steps over the screen is controlled by controlling the height of each step of the pump generator; in this way the number of samples per division are adjusted. The output of the staircase generator is fed to the comparator via an attenuator and a variable-voltage source. A *time-scale magnifier* is controlled by the attenuator. If the staircase voltage is attenuated before it is compared with the ramp, the ramp voltage reaches this lower staircase level more quickly and a sample is taken earlier. But since the staircase generator still gives the same step, the next step (= sample) on the screen represents a shorter time also. It will be clear that by adding a dc voltage in series with one input of the comparator, a shift in horizontal direction or *time position* will result on the screen.

At the end of each sweep, the staircase generator is reset (internally). Simultaneously, a blanking pulse is fed to the blanking mixer and in turn to the CRT. In this way blanking between each sweep is accomplished. The pump circuit also supplies pulses to the blanking mixer. These pulses are used for blanking during the staircase transients. Other horizontal modes, such as single scan, x EXT, and manual scan, can be obtained also by means of the HORIZONTAL MODE switch.

Block Diagram of a Sampling Oscilloscope

Refer to the simplified block diagram in Fig. 3.22. As this is a dual-trace oscilloscope, there is a need for a trigger selector. The trigger selector allows the trigger signal to be chosen from the Y_A or Y_B channels, or from an external source (EXT TRIG IN).

For vertical deflection, the signal from the memory amplifiers is fed via an electronic switch to the vertical plates of the CRT. This switch determines whether the displayed signal is signal $A, B, A + B, A - B, A$ and B, or A and $-B$. It is even possible to set A VERT, and B HOR. In this case the B-channel signal from the memory amplifier is used to drive the horizontal deflection.

Again reference to the block diagram (Fig. 3.22) shows that the oscilloscope has four signal outputs. The A output provides the signal in channel A, and the B output for channel B, while the Y output provides the signal coming from the Y amplifier, depending on the setting of the display-mode selector. The latter signal may be $A + B, A - B, A, B$, or A and B, or A and $-B$. The X output provides the signal fed to the comparator, which may be the staircase voltage (NORMAL), the dc voltage (MANUAL SCAN), the external X signal (X-EXT) or the slow signal (SINGLE), depending on the setting of the X-deflection mode selector. In position A VERT and B HOR the X output still gives the signals mentioned, but not the B signal. The amplitude of all output signals is 0.5 V/cm deflection on the screen. The zero levels of the A, B, and Y signals correspond to the center of the screen, while that of the X signal corresponds to the left-hand side of the screen.

Extra Applications Only Possible with the Sampling Oscilloscope

Recording Signals with an *X-Y* Recorder

One of the limitations of an oscilloscope is the relatively small size of the screen (generally 8×10 cm). If the trace is 0.3 mm thick, this gives a resolution of about 270×330 lines. A photographic record of the trace

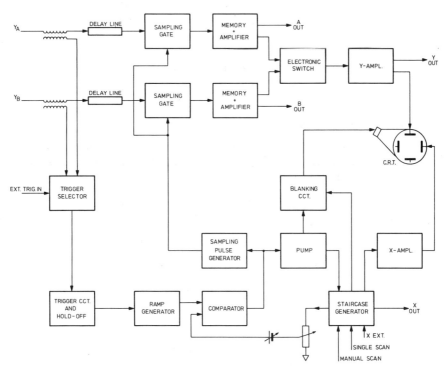

Fig. 3.22 Complete block diagram of a dual-channel sequential-sampling oscilloscope.

on the screen will be subject to the same limitations as regards resolution, while making extra copies of Polaroid prints (the usual medium used in oscilloscope cameras) is by no means an easy matter, and is relatively expensive.

As explained previously, under Random Sampling versus Sequential Sampling, the sampling oscilloscope can be considered as a low-frequency oscilloscope, once the samples have been taken. As a matter of fact a so-called scan conversion has taken place. Since the sampling oscilloscope can enlarge signal details to a much greater extent than a normal oscilloscope, the sampling oscilloscope can be compared to a microscope.

Additionally, if we connect one of the vertical outputs and the X output of the PM 3400 oscilloscope to an X-Y recorder, we can get a recording of the signal on the screen of the CRT. A Polaroid photo and an X-Y recording of the same signal are shown in Fig. 3.23. On the recording, 2 cm correspond to 1 cm on the oscilloscope screen, while the line width is about the same in both cases.

The resolution of the X-Y recording will be about twice as good as that of the Polaroid oscillogram. Furthermore, the X-Y recording has the advantage that it can be made on graph paper, thus making amplitude and time measurements much faster and more accurate.

Finally, the X-Y recordings can be reproduced with normal copying equipment. This gives excellent, very cheap prints, which can be an important consideration when a large number of copies of the recording are needed, for example as educational material in schools and universities.

The Accurate Measurement of Signals

The independence of the sweep of the PM 3400 oscilloscope from the time scale can be very effectively used for high-accuracy measurements of hf signals. The signal in question is simply displayed on the screen and switched over to MANUAL SCAN, the spot manually adjusted to the point on the trace of interest, and the amplitude of the signal from the appropriate vertical output measured with a dc voltmeter.

The *linearity* of the amplitude ratio between the input and output signals was found, by measurement on a number of instruments, to be better than 0.2% for the middle 6 vertical divisions, measured between input and *Y output*. Measurements on the *A and B outputs* (Fig. 3.23) revealed a linearity of better than 0.05% for all 8 divisions. The difference in performance between the Y output and the A and B outputs is caused by a network in the Y amplifier which compensates for the slight nonlinearity of the CRT found at extreme vertical deflections. The A and B output signals are taken off before this compensation network.

The accuracy of the output voltage is $\pm 5\%$ and that of the V/cm control is ±3%, a total of ±8%. However, this error can be eliminated by introducing adjustable attenuation of the output signal to be measured. This attenuation can be calibrated by means of an accurately known dc voltage applied to the input of the oscilloscope, for example. In this way, the total error can be restricted to about 0.1%.

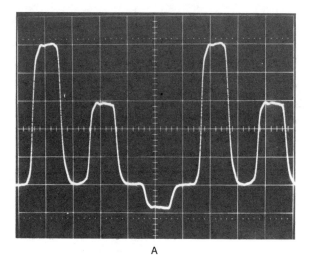

A

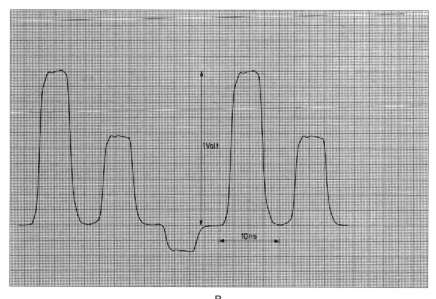

B

Fig. 3.23 Recording signals with an *X-Y* recorder. (*A*) Oscillogram of a fast rise-time signal with reflections (amplitude, 200 mV/div; time, 5 ns/div). (*B*) The signal of (*A*) recorded on an *X-Y* recorder; amplitude and time are shown in the graph.

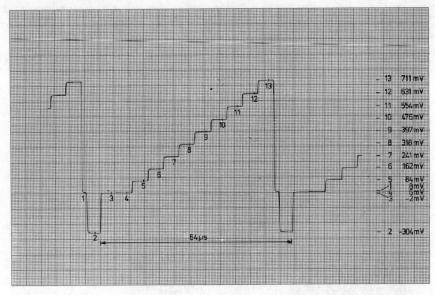

Fig. 3.24 Plotted display of a video staircase signal. (At the numbered points the accuracy is checked with a digital voltmeter.)

A very convenient way of making accurate measurements and recording a signal at the same time is shown in Fig. 3.24. The signal is first recorded on an *X-Y* recorder in the SINGLE SCAN mode. Then, in the MANUAL SCAN mode, the spot is positioned at the point of interest and the OUTPUT signal is accurately measured. At the same time the pen lift of the recorder can be released so that an extra dot is obtained on the recording at the point in question. This procedure can then be repeated for other points on the signal.

Applications of this type are possible not only for signals with frequencies of several hundred MHz but also for signals of only a few kHz. In fact, it is possible to measure every part of a signal up to 200 μs (corresponding to the slowest time/distance setting of 20 μs/cm) after a trigger point, provided the repetition rate of the signal is about 10 Hz or more.

Measurements on Signals below the Noise Level

The use of a recorder for handling the output signals of the PM 3400 oscilloscope has the advantage of acting as a low-pass filter that effectively reduces noise and jitter. It has been found possible to measure signals that lie considerably below the noise level in this way. Figure 3.25 shows the block diagram of a setup which can be used for this purpose. As can be seen from the diagram, the signal used for the experiment is also applied to the EXT TRIG IN input of the oscilloscope. When a signal containing noise is measured in this way, the amplitude of the samples will have random values. The average amplitude will thus be zero. Recording signals on an X-Y recording via a sampling oscilloscope will give a considerable reduction of the noise because the X-Y recorder acts as an integrator. If, however, the noise signal contains a component which is coupled in frequency with the trigger signal, this part of the signal is recorded without attenuation.

The results obtainable with such a setup are illustrated in Figs. 3.26 and 3.27. Figure 3.26 shows the oscillogram of a signal with noise, while Fig. 3.27 shows the X-Y recording of the same signal, as taken from the vertical output of the PM 3400 oscilloscope. As the repetition rate of the trigger signal determines the sampling frequency, the samples will follow low-frequency noise components. Such noise will thus give a residual signal on the recording.

An extra integrating network between the oscilloscope and the recorder can be used to give further attenuation of these lf noise components, but the signal will then have to be scanned more slowly. Otherwise, the signal itself will be affected by the integrating network.

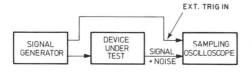

Fig. 3.25 Measuring setup for signals below the noise level.

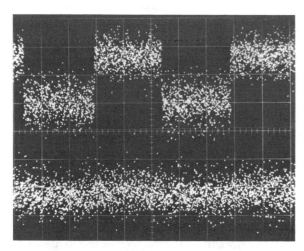

Fig. 3.26 Double exposure. (Upper trace) A pulse signal with a signal-to-noise ratio of about 1. (Lower trace) The signal is attenuated $10\times$ (-20 dB) while the noise remained the same.

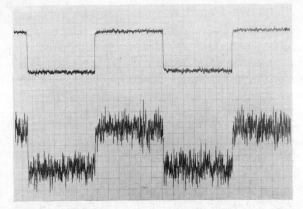

Fig. 3.27 Reduction of noise caused by the integrating X-Y recorder. Both upper and lower traces are the same as shown in Fig. 3.26. The magnification at the paper with respect to the screen to 2.5×.

The Sampling Scope in the Development of Magnetic-Bubble Devices

Introduction Magnetic bubbles—cylindrical magnetic domains with a diameter of the order of 5 μm—in garnet films show promise for applications in such devices as computer memories and display and recording systems. Such bubbles are surrounded by a circular magnetic-domain wall. It is important to be able to measure the velocity of domain walls and bubbles in the development work on such devices, and the Philips sampling oscilloscope PM 3400 has been playing an essential role in such measurements.

The Experiment The setup for a measurement of the velocity of a magnetic domain wall used in Philips' Research Laboratories is shown in Fig. 3.29 and in the block diagram (Fig. 3.28). The position of the wall is made visible in a polarizing microscope by the Faraday effect. The displacement of the wall can be followed by measuring the intensity of the light transmitted in the microscope with a photomultiplier. The photomultiplier output is amplified and passed to the sampling scope.

The signal-to-noise ratio can be improved by a factor of about 30, by using the sampling scope as a boxcar integrator. In this mode, the horizontal sweep is driven externally by a ramp voltage obtained from a battery and a motor-driven potentiometer (scanner). The motor speed is adjusted so that a complete horizontal scan is completed in about 5 *minutes*. With this slow sweep, the improvement in the signal-to-noise ratio can be obtained simply by feeding the vertical output voltage of the oscilloscope to the *Y* input of an *X-Y* recorder via an *RC* network with a typi-

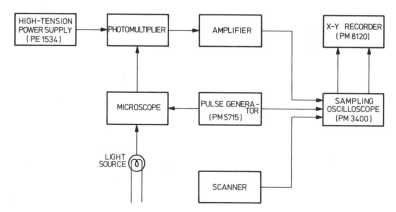

Fig. 3.28 Block diagram of measuring arrangement shown in Fig. 3.29.

Fig. 3.29 A typical setup for a measurement of the velocity of a magnetic domain wall used in Philips Research Laboratories.

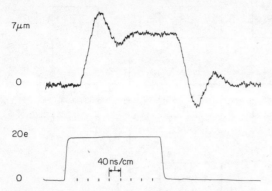

Fig. 3.30 Record of domain wall displacement.

cal time constant of 1 s. This network then serves as a noise filter. The X output of the oscilloscope is connected directly to the X input of the recorder. An example of a domain-wall displacement is shown in the upper curve of Fig. 3.30. In the lower curve the wall drive field is given. This field is superimposed on a constant field radiant (not shown).

3.3 SPECIAL OSCILLOSCOPE VARIANTS

The Multiplier Oscilloscope

One of the latest oscilloscope features is the multiplication of signals. With this it is possible to study instantaneous power. For instance, during the switching transients in logic circuitry, the collector voltage can be seen as a function of time. Also, the collector current can be shown on the screen. The product of these parameters is then a measure of the collector dissipation. But it is difficult to study the instantaneous power from the screen. For this the analog multiplier provides a solution.

Analog multiplication is by no means new. In early days it was performed in analog computers with the aid of operational amplifiers equipped with tubes. Hence the circuitry suffered from drift. The principle was simple: *quarter-square multiplication*. Both the sum and the difference of the signals V_A and V_B to be multiplied were squared (by diode/resistor networks), then subtracted and scaled according to

$$(V_A + V_B)^2 - (V_A - V_B)^2 = 4V_A V_B$$

Other techniques were also used.

The introduction of *monolithic integrated circuits* eliminated most of the imperfections of the older multiplier. Use is made of the fact that matched pairs of transistors can be produced easily with a very high degree of equality. The type of multiplier discussed in the following paragraphs is the type used in the Philips range of oscilloscopes.

The heart of the multiplier is the *gain cell,* shown in Fig. 3.31. For this circuit it can be mathematically derived that the current ratio

$$\frac{I_1}{I_2} = \frac{1 + a}{1 - a}$$

Thus the ratio of the collector currents I_1 and I_2 is determined by the ratio of the *external* currents forced through D_1 and D_2. Hence the term *current-ratio multiplier* is often met. It should be noted that the *ratio* is independent of the bias current I, because it does not appear in the above equation. If, in Fig. 3.31, the diode currents are modulated by one signal, v_A, and the bias current I with a second signal, v_B, then the output currents I_1 and I_2 will contain a product term of the two signals. It can be seen clearly if we express the equation

$$I_1 = \frac{a + 1}{2} I$$

where $I = I_1 + I_2$.

But a phenomenon is also vital for obtaining a *product;* that is, the *transconductance* of the transistors is proportional to the collector current. Due to the second property the term *variable-transconductance multiplier* is met also, although this term does not refer explicitly to the circuit in Fig. 3.31 only.

In order to suit the circuit for all polarity combinations of the input signals, the same principle as in Fig. 3.31 is used twice. The result is then called a *four-quadrant multiplier* (see Fig. 3.32). If the modulation of the diode currents $I_D (1 - a)$ and $I_D (1 + a)$ comes from the output of a differential amplifier with an input voltage v_A, and in the same way the bias currents $I (1 - b)$ and $I (1 + b)$ from an input voltage v_B, then the output voltage developed across the collector resistors R may be written as

$$v_{\text{out}} = K \cdot v_A \cdot v_B$$

with K being a constant factor determined by the circuit components.

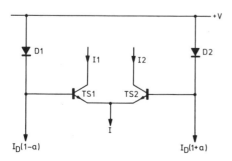

Fig. 3.31 The current-ratioing cell.

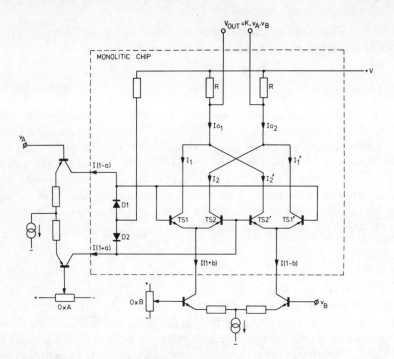

Fig. 3.32 A four-quadrant multiplier.

Note: As already stated, this multiplier could only be produced with the use of monolithic integrated circuits. For example, it is supposed that all junction temperatures are equal and that all transistors are exactly the same.

At the front panel of the oscilloscope two new control knobs OXA and OXB are present. These controls are used to balance out any dc components present at the multiplier inputs. These dc components may come from the input preamplifiers (see Fig. 2.9). Because of the special drift-compensation circuits in these amplifiers, these balance controls seldom need to be readjusted.

The incorporation of the multiplier into an oscilloscope may be realized as shown in the block diagram, Fig. 3.33, which applies to the Philips oscilloscope PM 3265. The electronic switch in channel A is in the $A \times B$ mode. The channel A signal is fed to the multiplier as is the channel B signal, and the output of the multiplier is fed to the electronic channel selector. By means of this selector, the display at the screen can be:

- A only
- B only
- A and B alternate
- A and B chopped

- $A + B$ (position ADD)
- $A \times B$ (position MULTIPLY)
- $A \times B$ and B chopped or alternate

In this last position the chopped or alternate mode is dependent on the MTB TIME/DIV setting. From 0.5 s to 2 ms it is automatically switched to the chopped mode, and from 1 ms to 2 μs it is in the alternate mode. The considerations for this choice are the same as discussed in Sec. 2.3.

In the upper position of the switch (Fig. 3.33) the channel A signal is fed directly to the channel-mode selector and the multiplier is not in use. The output of the channel selector is fed to the delay line and from there to the CRT vertical deflection plates via the final Y amplifier (see Fig. 2.9). A second output from the channel-mode selector leads to the composite signal amplifier. This amplifier provides two signals:

1. The product $A \times B$ to a BNC rear connector (Y OUT) of the oscilloscope. It may be used for other purposes (see Fig. 3.34).

2. A composite trigger signal for the MTB. An advantage of this is described in Sec. 2.6.

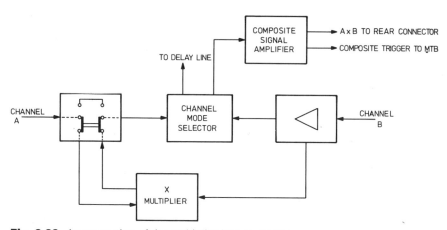

Fig. 3.33 Incorporation of the multiplier into an oscilloscope.

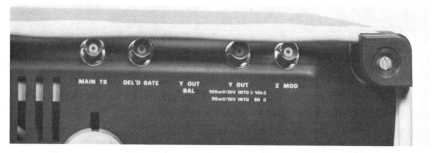

Fig. 3.34 The multiplier output is available at the Y OUT socket at the rear of the oscilloscope.

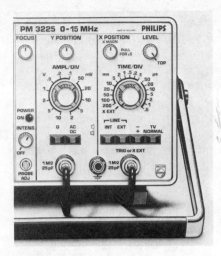

Fig. 3.35 Front-panel layout of the Philips PM 3225 oscilloscope, showing the provision for TV triggering.

As previously mentioned, typical applications can be found in power measurements of switching transients in digital circuits, but also in switched sine-wave thyristor control, phase detection, frequency doubling, and so on. Some measuring examples are given in Chap. 6.

TV Triggering

The study of TV signals may be required both in the field and in laboratory. For the ease of operation a TV sync separator may be built into an oscilloscope. The synchronization pulse separator (sync separator) provides two types of trigger pulses for the oscilloscope:

1. Line trigger pulses derived from the TV line sync pulses which are present at each line from which the TV picture is built up.

2. Field trigger pulses derived every time a completely new TV picture (field) is started.

The extra provisions and their operating controls are described in the following paragraphs.

In the smaller (service) oscilloscopes the provision may be extremely simple. Figure 3.35 shows the front-panel layout of the single-trace Philips PM 3225 oscilloscope. The trigger-source selector switch is set in either the NORMAL mode or in the TV mode. In the TV mode the selection of a TV line or a TV field trigger pulse is *automatically* coupled with the

TIME/DIV setting. From 0.5 ms/div down to 200 ms/div, the TV field is chosen; from 0.2 ms/div up to 0.5 μs/div, TV line triggering takes place.

Depressing the ± pushbutton permits the oscilloscope to accept both positive and negative polarity of the composite video signal. The word "LINE" above "INT" and "EXT" on the front panel indicates triggering on the line or mains frequency (50 or 60 Hz).

In the larger (laboratory) oscilloscopes the provisions, and also the selection criteria, for TV triggering are a little more complicated. Part of the front-panel layout of the Philips 50-MHz oscilloscope PM 3240X is shown in Fig. 3.36. An extra position, TV, is added to the trigger coupling switch in the main-time-base section. When the TV and HF push buttons are depressed, triggering of the MTB occurs at the TV line sync pulse (TVL). Similarly, the combination of TV and LF causes triggering at the TV field sync pulses (TVF). Again the word "LINE" at the trigger source selector switch on the front panel indicates triggering at the line or mains frequency.

Fig. 3.36 Detail of front panel of Philips PM 3240X oscilloscope, showing the provisions for TV triggering.

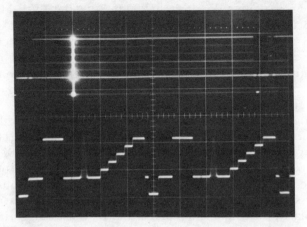

Fig. 3.37 Double exposure of a TV signal. Upper trace shows full field in the MTB mode. In the lower trace the intensified part indicates selected lines which are displayed with the oscilloscope in the DTB mode.

Depending upon the polarity of the composite video signal, the LEVEL/ SLOPE pushbutton must be in the appropriate position (IN + or OUT −). The MTB trigger-level control is not in operation when the TV pushbutton is depressed.

The delayed-time-base section has TVL facility also. If the TVL pushbutton is depressed, the delayed time base is triggered by the TV line sync pulses, assuming that the MTB is operating in the TV mode. In the TVL mode of the DTB both the trigger level control and the slope (IN + or OUT −) are not in operation.

The DTB in the TVL mode functions as the trigger in the normal mode (see Sec. 2.15). When the DTB is activated (the TIME/DIV switch moved from its OFF position) and the MTB is displayed, then the TV line of interest in the TV field may be selected (intensified on the screen) with the DELAY TIME multiplier, after which pushing the DEL'D TB button results in a triggered display of the selected TV line. This is illustrated in a double-exposed photograph (Fig. 3.37). The upper trace shows the intensified part of a full-field TV test signal which is displayed by the DTB mode in the lower trace.

The Four-Channel Oscilloscope

There are many applications where the measuring time of a device under test can be considerably reduced by using a four-channel oscilloscope. This is particularly true in the case of digital and computer applications. Also, in education a four-channel oscilloscope can be of great help. For example, the operation of a three-input NAND gate can be observed from the screen in one glance (see Fig. 3.38). The extra controls and display modes with respect to the normal dual-trace oscilloscope are described in the following paragraphs.

Figure 3.39 shows all the operating controls appropriate to the vertical channels of the Philips PM 3244 four-channel oscilloscope. The vertical display mode is selected by the six-way pushbutton switch A, $A + B$, B, C, $C + D$, and D. Up to four channels can be displayed by depressing one or more of the pushbuttons A, B, C, or D. Two more traces can be displayed by depressing the $A + B$ and $C + D$ pushbuttons, so that altogether six traces from four channels can be displayed. Furthermore, each channel can be inverted by pulling the center knobs of the AMPL/DIV switches which, in combination with the pushbuttons $A + B$ and $C + D$, also provide $\pm A \pm B$ and $\pm C \pm D$ display facilities. The channels can be either chopped (CHOP) at a free running rate of about 1 MHz or switched to the next channel at the end of each sweep (ALT).

Trigger-source selection for both the main time base and the delayed time base can be from any channel (A, B, C, or D) or from a combined signal after the electronic switch (COMPOSITE) (see Fig. 3.40). The main time base can also be triggered from an externally applied signal (EXT) or from a signal derived from the line voltage (LINE). The HOLD OFF control

Fig. 3.38 The use of a four-trace oscilloscope enables the operation of a three-input NAND gate to be completely checked in one measurement.

Fig. 3.39 Operating controls appropriate to the vertical channels; up to six traces of four channels can be selected.

Fig. 3.40 Extensive trigger selection possibilities obviate the need to change and rechange probe connections in order to obtain the correct trigger source.

can be set to prevent the occurrence of double-picture displays on complex waveforms (see also Sec. 2.11).

Horizontal deflection can be supplied by any of the sources (A, B, C, D, LINE, or EXT) that can be selected for triggering the main time base.

Many examples using the four-channel oscilloscope in digital and computer applications are described in Chapter 6 of the Philips publication "Zeroing in on ones and zeros."

The DTB with Digital Delay

In a previous paragraph it was seen that the delayed time base is started (or triggered) when the MTB sweep has reached a certain level which is compared to a preset dc level. The preset level is thus reached a certain *time* after the MTB has started. This time is determined by the TIME/DIV setting of the MTB. If the signal possesses a jitter, the display of the DTB will not be stable when operated in the START mode. Usually, selecting the TRIG mode of the DTB will eliminate this trouble. If, however, the jitter is considerable, it can exceed the time between two adjacent waveforms. This may be the case with mechanical devices, such as tape or disk units of computer systems. Not even in the TRIG mode of the DTB can a unique display be obtained, because one delayed sweep may be triggered at waveform number 67 and the next one may be at waveform number 69. If all waveforms are identical (pulses), however, the display will be stable, although the observer will not know which pulse he or she is looking at.

The timing diagram, Fig. 3.41, is exaggerated to illustrate the effect of digital delay if jitter is too excessive. Between pulses number 6 and 7 a disturbance is to be studied on the screen. Triggering of the MTB is always supposed to occur at pulse 0. The DELAY time is set as at D in the illustration. Due to the jitter the delayed sweep at E is triggered by pulse 6 and at F by pulse 5. In the latter case the disturbance is not even displayed.

To overcome this problem in the Philips PM 3261 oscilloscope, a preset counter is built in. With the aid of front-panel control knobs this counter can be preset to any value between 0000 and 9999. The counter is reset at the end of each sweep of the MTB. At the beginning of each MTB sweep, the counter starts counting the number of DTB trigger pulses. As soon as the preset number is reached, the DTB sweep is triggered. In this way the pulses are now identified by their *number* and not by their *time* with respect to a starting point.

Timing diagrams are given in Fig. 3.42. After the hold-off period of the MTB sweep, the next MTB sweep is started at pulse 0 in Fig. 3.42. From this diagram it can be seen that the reset multivibrator (REM) of the DTB is set ready at pulse $(n - 1)$ when pulse n has to be displayed.

The first DTB trigger pulse will then start the DTB sweep. Obviously, a reference signal must also be present to start the MTB and, in turn, the

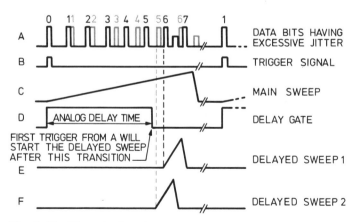

Fig. 3.41 When the jitter is more than the distance between adjacent pulses, problems occur even if the DTB is in the triggered mode. Digital delay solves this problem by identifying pulses by their count.

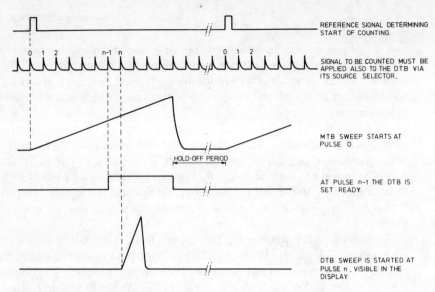

Fig. 3.42 Timing diagram illustrating the effect of digital delay.

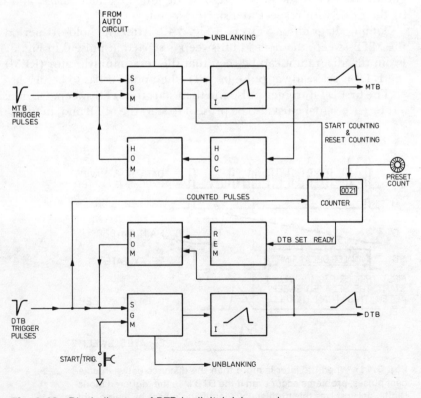

Fig. 3.43 Block diagram of DTB in digital delay mode.

counting procedure. The reference signal must be lower in frequency than the signal to be counted (see Fig. 3.42).

A block diagram of the MTB and DTB switched for operating in the DIGITAL DELAY mode is shown in Fig. 3.43 (compare with Fig. 2.24). Both the information to start counting and to reset the counter are taken from the MTB sweep-gating multivibrator (SGM). By differentiating the SGM pulse, the beginning and the end of the pulse (and by this the MTB sweep) can be distinguished. Figure 3.44 shows the front-panel arrangement of the Philips PM 3261 oscilloscope, which incorporates digital delay. The number of the pulse or event at which the DTB is to be triggered is shown by a LED display. The PRESET COUNT knob shown in Fig. 3.43 is identified only by COUNT in Fig. 3.44. Also an extra pushbutton, DIGITAL DELAY, is provided. By depressing this button, the display will indicate 0001. Any preset value to 9999 can now be set by the COUNT control. This control can be set to count up or to count down at a speed which is determined by the position of the control knob. The further the COUNT control is turned away from its midposition, the faster the counting will be. The count range varies from 1 count per 2 seconds to 60 counts per second. The counting speed can be increased to range from

Fig. 3.44 Front-panel arrangement of the Philips PM 3261 oscilloscope. Only one extra control knob operates the digital delay. All normal functions are available when the DIGITAL DELAY pushbutton is not depressed.

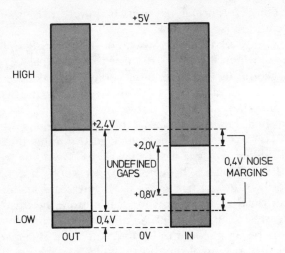

Fig. 3.45 TTL definition levels for both input and output at the TTL devices.

15 to 1500 counts per second by pulling out the COUNT knob. The variable count rate not only enables the operator to set the preset value quickly, but also allows him or her to examine a train of pulses, or a block of data bits, step by step at a convenient speed. Turning back the COUNT control knob into its midposition stops counting. The intensified part of the picture can be displayed magnified in the DELAYED time-base mode. Further information and application examples are given in the Philips publication "Zeroing in on ones and zeros."

TTL Triggering

In logic systems employing building blocks (gates, flip-flops, etc.), a logic state level may be defined in order to determine whether a logic signal is supposed to be in its 0 (zero) or in its 1 state. When TTL (transistor-transistor logic) is applied, the levels are defined as shown in Fig. 3.45.

A distinction is made between the input and output of a device. The maximum voltage is the *low* state at the *output* (0.4 V) of a device is below the maximum level which is recognized also as *low* at the input (0.8 V) of the following device. In the same way the minimum *high* level at the output (2.4 V) is always higher than the level which is recognized as *high* at the input (2.0 V). These differences (both 0.4 V) are defined in this way as a "noise margin" to reduce the influence of noise. In this way the TTL circuits are to these extents made immune to noise or interfering signals.

For the same reasons of immunity to noise on the TTL signals, a digital oscilloscope, as already described, may be provided with TTL trigger-level coupling. It can be seen from Fig. 3.44 that the trigger coupling modes of the MTB are TTL-DC-AC. Consequently, the choice lf-hf is reduced to ac (see Fig. 2.11) with the addition of TTL. When the TTL trigger mode is selected, the trigger circuit responds in the same way as the input of a TTL building block. In this mode also the LEVEL control knob of the MTB is not in operation. The SLOPE selection (+ or −) remains, so that triggering at both positive and negative transients is still possible.

In order to reduce capacitive loading of the measuring point (see Chap. 4), it is advisable always to operate with a 10:1 probe on TTL circuits. For the *internal* trigger sources (channel *A* or *B*) this means that an input sensitivity setting of 0.1 V/div always results in a stable display of TTL signals. In the external (EXT) trigger mode a 10:1 probe is required to adapt TTL levels to the EXT trigger input.

Example: Figure 3.46 shows the TTL switching levels of an oscilloscope in the TTL trigger mode. The levels of the margins are those of a TTL device input (compare Fig. 3.45). As long as the input signals remain within these margins, a stable display is guaranteed in the TTL trigger mode. A normal trigger-level setting might cause ambiguous displays. This is demonstrated in Fig. 3.47*A* and *B*.

Frequently, probes are connected to logic circuits without proper grounding. The inductance of a ground lead which is too long and the probe's capacitance together form a series resonant circuit that is excited by the switching transitions in the logic, causing considerable ringing. This ringing is demonstrated in Fig. 3.47*A*, where the probe's ground lead is left ungrounded.

Ringing may provide many trigger points in the normal trigger mode when the LEVEL control is not set correctly, causing an ambiguous display, such as shown in Fig. 3.47*B*. A TTL trigger mode obviates the need for any LEVEL setting and thus results in a proper display in most cases.

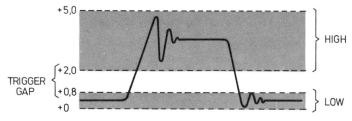

Fig. 3.46 TTL triggering makes the oscilloscope to some extent immune to noise or ringing present in the trigger signal.

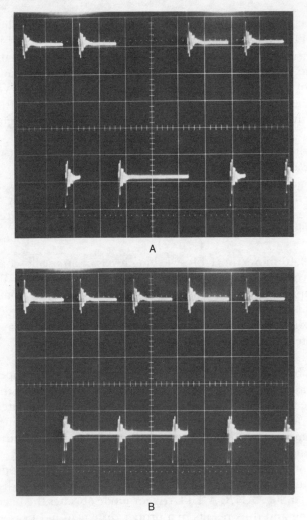

A

B

Fig. 3.47 Illustrations of ambiguous displays with normal trigger-level setting. In A and B the TIME/DIV settings are 1 μs/div. (A) Ringing caused by the probe not being properly grounded. (B) A display caused by false triggering. To prevent this, setting or resetting the LEVEL control is necessary, which is obviated by the trigger mode facility.

The Logic Analyzer

Within the scope of this book the logic analyzer will be treated very briefly, because the only points of correspondence that it has in common with an oscilloscope are the CRT and the word that is most frequently used in relation to both instruments: *triggering*. As a matter of fact the oscilloscope and the logic analyzer are totally different instruments and one cannot replace the other. On the contrary, they complement each other in digital techniques. This will be understood when the differences in setup are considered.

Even when used to display digital information, the oscilloscope starts displaying all information after a certain trigger instant. This applies also for the storage oscilloscope. The only shift in time of the display with respect to the trigger instant, is caused by the delay line in the vertical channel. This delay has been built in in order to visualize the leading edge of a pulse-shaped waveform (see Sec. 2.5). Furthermore, the real-time oscilloscope is basically an analog instrument for the display of signals in the time domain.

On the other hand, the logic analyzer is a digital instrument, especially developed for applications in the microcomputer field. It can represent digital information both in the time domain and in the data domain. Unlike an oscilloscope, not only can it display information *after* a certain trigger instant, but also *before* this point in time. For this purpose the logic analyzer possesses in each "vertical channel" a pair of digital memories (registers), or 20 pairs if the instrument has 20 input channels. At a trigger command the contents of one of the two memories in each channel remains preserved for display purposes. This can be explained with the aid of the block diagram in Fig. 3.48.

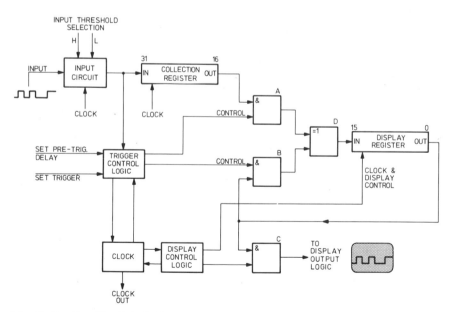

Fig. 3.48 Simplified block diagram of a logic-analyzer input channel.

Here we see first an input circuit which may be adjustable for several types of digital input level (TTL-CMOS-ECL). This level can be set by dc voltages at the H (= high) and L (= low) line. The whole system operates at a clock rate (internally clocked), meaning that this is an example of a so-called asynchronous analyzer. With the maximum clock rate the time resolution is also determined. The higher the clock rate, the more samples of the digital input signal can be taken per unit of time and the higher the resolution of the display. A maximum resolution as high as 15 ns at a clock rate of 100 MHz can be obtained. Note that the rate of display can be, and usually is, much lower than may be suggested by these figures. For example, one sweep at the display may last 100 μs (time-domain measurement).

In Fig. 3.48 the data are first accumulated in a shift register, before they are transferred into the display register. This shift procedure takes as many as clock pulses as the bit length of the register (16 in the example of Fig. 3.48). Once the data information is in the display registers, we can preserve it and let it circulate by feeding back its output signal to the input. This is controlled by the display control logic, which closes AND gate A while opening B. Via gate C the same signal becomes available for display purpose.

As mentioned above, the display can be formatted in the time domain or in the data domain. Both possibilities are shown in the demonstration setup of Fig. 3.49. The lower oscilloscope shows two of the signals (only two input channels) in the time domain, while the picture on the upper screen is formatted in the data domain. The actual analyzer is placed besides the oscilloscopes, which are used as a display unit here. Compact analyzers exist as well of course.

Finally, the displaying of pretrigger information will be discussed. Suppose that, after a trigger impulse at the set trigger input of the trigger control logic, the collection of data in the collection register is delayed for, say, 11 clock pulses (via the set pretrigger delay input). This means that after the trigger moment 11 bits are still collected (posttrigger bits). But since the register in Fig. 3.48 is 16 bits long, 5 pretrigger bits are still present in the register. When this information is transferred to the display register, the result on the screen will be a display of 5 pretrigger bits and 11 posttrigger bits. A vertical cursor over the whole screen, along with a digital number, indicate the bit at which it is triggered. It should be clear that this way of presentation of digital information can never be accomplished by a plain real-time oscilloscope.

Of the many operation modes of the logic analyzer, two will be mentioned here. At this point it must be borne in mind that the block diagram in Fig. 3.48 is just a simple example used to explain the basic operation. The registers can be switched to other configurations as well, in order to perform other measurements.

One way of operation is to recognize a digital word of n parallel bits. For this, n of the input channels are used. The inputs of these n channels are preset in combination of L (= low), H (= high), and/or "don't care." As soon as such a combination is also met at the n input wires, a trigger pulse is generated, after which a stable display is generated. A number of pretrigger bits may be selected as well. The trigger criterion is thus the equality of the presented (= measured) word and the preselected combination of the n bits in parallel formatting the parallel word.

This principle of the "word recognizer" is shown in Fig. 3.50. The intensified data information on the left-hand side on the screen shows the differences with the information (previously measured) shown at the right-hand side. In Chap. 4 we will see that the logic trigger probe operates on the same principle to initiate a trigger pulse.

Another possibility then is serial word recognition. The analyzer "looks" to the latest n bits received at one channel and compares the pattern with a preset serial word at another channel. A trigger pulse is generated when equality exists. The preset serial word may be measured and stored previous to the search for recognition.

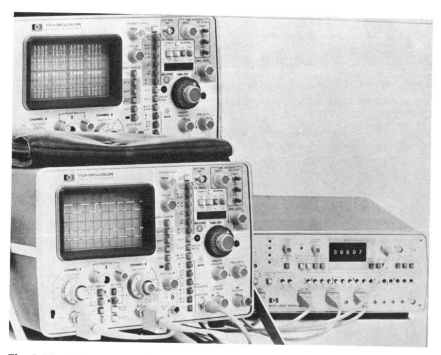

Fig. 3.49 With new State Display "Gold Button" option and logic-state analyzer, Hewlett-Packard oscilloscope instantly interchanges displays of data stream in the time domain and data domain. (*Photograph courtesy of Hewlett-Packard Benelux N.V.— Netherlands.*)

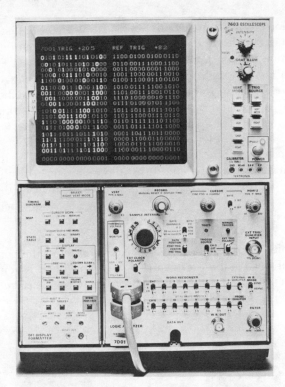

Fig. 3.50 Logic-analyzer unit with the possibility of word recognizing. (*Photograph courtesy of Tektronix Holland N.V.*)

Note: Out of the many possible pitfalls in reading logic analyzer specifications, one is mentioned here. In order to be able to perform measurements, one has to connect the logic analyzer to the device under text. This can be done via cables or via special probes. A question that may arise, however, is whether the analyzer's manufacturer has such a probe as an accessory or not. Furthermore, the termination of such a probe is essential because very fast transients have to be detected. And if the probe is terminated, what will be the loading effect of the probe on the circuit under test? So, not only do the analyzer's specs have to be analyzed, but also those of the probe to match. This is a pitfall that is often overlooked.

Plug-in Oscilloscopes

The pros and cons of plug-in oscilloscopes with respect to compact oscilloscopes are discussed here.

A plug-in oscilloscope is electrically like any other oscilloscope. The mechanical housing of the plug-in instrument is different from that of the compact one, because the former consists of a main frame to which one or more plug-in units can be added, to vary the oscilloscope's facilities. The company which has elaborated the plug-in idea the most by far is Tektronix, Inc. Figure 3.51 shows an example demonstrating the idea.

The choice between a plug-in or a compact oscilloscope can be aggravated by the question:

How many different oscilloscope functions do I need, and for how many people?

Let us explain the answers to this question with the aid of some cases.

If someone has to equip a small laboratory staff (about 4 to 6 engineers) which has to fulfill a great variety of R&D jobs, the preference will be for plug-in oscilloscopes. Now, everyone can have a main frame with his or her own standard plug-ins. However, for the laboratory as a whole, a number of different special functions can be bought as plug-in units, which are cheaper per item than a complete oscilloscope.

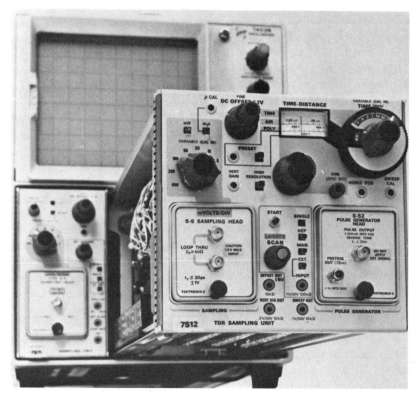

Fig. 3.51 Photograph showing the plug-in idea. Note that the Sampling Head and Pulse Generator Head themselves are again plugged in into the plug-in unit. (*Photograph courtesy of Tektronix Holland N.V.*)

If, on the other hand, a classroom has to be equipped with many of the same oscilloscopes (that is, functions), the compact oscilloscope is the one and only choice, because for the same function a compact is cheaper than the mechanically more complicated plug-in instrument.

If an engineer is the only electronic specialist in the department, the choice will depend on whether the kind of work requires a plug-in or a compact oscilloscope. In the service field a 15 to 25 MHz dual-channel compact oscilloscope usually is sufficient. For really electronic development work, a plug-in system is advisable. In the bigger radio and TV service workshops the same kind of work is done by all the engineers; a compact oscilloscope is the best choice here.

So far, all the considerations have related to the application fields. Of course, there are also price or price-performance motives that affect the choice between plug-in and compact oscilloscopes. In general, the compact oscilloscope is a mechanically simpler setup and hence cheaper (i.e., if the same functions are to be performed by oscilloscopes from the same company). Moreover, once a plug-in system is set up in a laboratory, one is more or less obliged to continue with it, because the purchase of an additional compact oscilloscope would make the plug-in system more expensive. Some parts of the compact oscilloscope would have been bought superfluously.

Because of the advanced technology in electronics, it is possible to create plug-in units for several kinds of functions, for example, frequency counter, digital voltmeter, spectrum analyzer, time-domain reflectometer, and lately, the logic analyzer (see Fig. 3.50). Of course, these all are eminent developments, but there is a catch. The specs of the frequency-counter plug-in unit can only compete with those of a moderate compact counter. The same applies for the DVM function and so on.

It makes sense, then, to set up a plug-in system in a lab as long as one realizes what he or she is buying. Don't think that it is cheaper to buy only the plug-in units as an extra to the oscilloscope, thereby avoiding having to buy the more expensive special instruments. Besides this, what do you do if you need three or more similar functions in one measuring setup and have only one plug-in oscilloscope? To overcome this problem, special power-supply units are produced into which several plug-in units can be inserted. But then this combination cannot really compete any more with the price-performance ratio of compact instruments.

Finally, what do you do if you have your special plug-in unit in your hands but need a second main frame which is not at hand? These problems do arise in practice.

However, in conclusion, a very strong point pleading for a plug-in system in a laboratory is the fact that all equipment comes from the same supplier. So only one sales person serves you and the after-sales service will be much better than when many instruments are bought from many different suppliers. Your lab has now become a good customer of that one supplier, and usually in such cases the service will be much quicker and smoother. Now, without calculating and expressing the profits thereof directly in money, it can be stated that good service saves a lot of time and thus a lot of money.

3.4 EXERCISES

For each exercise, circle the answer you believe is correct.

1. An advantage of the variable-persistence CRT over the bistable CRT is:

(A) The storage time is longer.

(B) The storage time is adjustable.

(C) It can be used in normal mode.

2. Which storage CRT has the highest writing speed?

(A) The bistable CRT

(B) The variable-persistence CRT

(C) The transfer-storage CRT

3. The advantage of a sampling oscilloscope is:

(A) Higher frequencies can be displayed.

(B) The display at the screen is more accurate.

(C) Shorter rise times can be displayed.

4. The smoothing control in a sampling oscilloscope allows:

(A) More samples per division on the screen

(B) Improvement of the signal-to-noise ratio of the display

(C) Better trigger stability

5. The multiplier oscilloscope has been developed for the:

(A) Display of instantaneous power

(B) Display of the rms value of voltages

(C) Possibility of composite triggering

6. Four frequency-related signals are displayed on a four-channel oscilloscope, $A = 1$ MHz, $B = 2$ MHz, $C = 4$ MHz, and $D = 8$ Mhz. Which signal must be selected for triggering?

(A) Does not matter

(B) Channel A

(C) Channel D

7. The digital delayed time base has been developed in order to:

   (A) Obtain a wider range of delay time.

   (B) Obtain a stable display even with excessive signal jitter.

   (C) Count the signal frequency.

8. An oscilloscope is provided with TTL triggering. As a result:

   (A) A stable display is guaranteed even with disturbed TTL trigger signals.

   (B) The capacitive loading of an *external* trigger source is reduced because a 10 : 1 probe must be used.

   (C) Both A and B.

OSCILLOSCOPE PROBES

4.1 INTRODUCTION

Normally oscilloscope specifications are given for the oscilloscope only and do not usually include auxiliary items such as probes. To connect the oscilloscope to the device under test, and to perform measurements, a variety of measuring leads and cables are available. The connecting leads and cables are usually referred to as *probes*. Because the probe and instrument connected together serves as the measuring setup, it should be noted that the probe is a very important link in this setup. Nevertheless, in many laboratories or service workshops the characteristics and behavior of the probes are often neglected. This chapter provides a basic understanding of the various types of probes and their applications. The material should help the engineer to choose the right type of probe for his or her particular needs.

Oscilloscope probes can be categorized into three main groups:

• Passive-voltage probes
• Active-voltage probes (FET probes)
• Dedicated probes

Each group will be discussed in turn in the following paragraphs.

4.2 PASSIVE-VOLTAGE PROBES

The most simple passive-voltage probe is a coaxial cable. But what actually happens when a coaxial cable is connected to the device under test? A schematic diagram of the test arrangement is given in Fig. 4.1. The device under test is symbolized as a signal source with an internal source resistance R_s.

For dc voltages there is no problem as long as $R_{in} \gg R_s$, because the part of E appearing at the input of the oscilloscope is

$$V_{osc} = \frac{R_{in}}{R_s + R_{in}} \cdot E$$

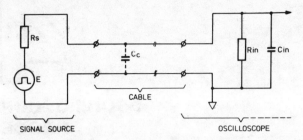

Fig. 4.1 Schematic circuit diagram showing a signal source connected to an oscilloscope by means of a coaxial cable.

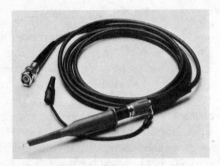

Fig. 4.2 A typical 1:1 passive-voltage probe.

But in applications involving ac voltages, the stray capacitances play an important role. Figure 4.1 shows the signal source loaded by R_{in} in parallel with $C_c + C_{in}$. As the impedance X_c of a capacitance is given by

$$X_c = \frac{1}{2\pi fC}$$

in which f is the frequency of the ac voltage, a relatively heavier loading of the signal source will occur at higher frequencies.

Example C_{in} is on the order of 14 to 21 pF, and for a coaxial cable of 1-m length, C_c is about 100 pF. At 1 MHz the impedance of $C_c + C_{in}$ is about 1.3 kΩ. Compared with a R_{in} of 1 MΩ (normally standardized), this means a heavy load.

From this example it will be realized that it is important to measure the voltage at a point in a circuit under test having a low source impedance, in order not to influence the circuit properties too much by the connection of the oscilloscope.

Figure 4.2 shows a typical coaxial cable. At one end a BNC connector is mounted for connection to the oscilloscope. The other end is provided with a special measuring clip (the probe tip) and a ground lead connector. This type of probe is a 1 : 1 probe because the signal is not attenuated by the probe. The cable capacitance of this type of probe may be in the order of magnitude as given in the example.

In cases where the cable capacitance of the 1 : 1 probe will be unacceptable, advantage can be taken of the 10 : 1 passive probe. Now the signal is attenuated 10 times by the probe. The schematic diagram is shown in Fig. 4.3. Basically, the object is to create for both dc and high frequencies a real 10 : 1 divider. This divider will be independent of the frequency for $RC = R_{in}C_{in}$.

As already mentioned, C_{in} can vary from 15 to 25 pF, depending on stray capacitances in the input circuitry of the oscilloscopes, which are, of course, not the same for every instrument. For this reason C is made variable.

A more realistic schematic diagram is given in Fig. 4.4, where compensation is for 120 pF, giving a value of $C = 13$ pF. At the probe tip there is also a stray capacitance C_s of about 2 to 4 pF from the tip itself to its environment. Effectively a total load capacitance of C_s parallel to C and $C_c + C_{in}$ in series is obtained, resulting in about 15 pF. But 15 pF is, nevertheless, far less than 120 pF. A disadvantage might be that the signal is attenuated 10 times at the input of the oscilloscope.

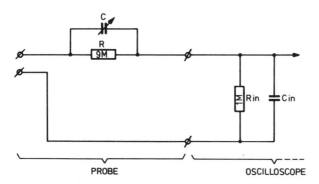

Fig. 4.3 Basic principle of a 10 : 1 divider probe.

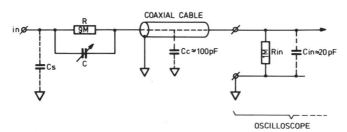

Fig. 4.4 The compensation network at the probe tip must also compensate for the capacitance of the probe cable.

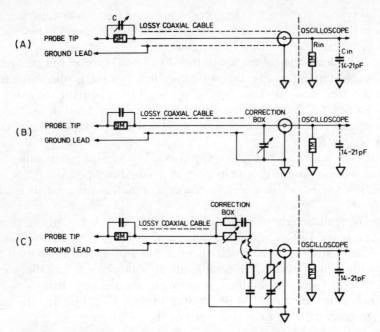

Fig. 4.5 Basic principles of a 10:1 passive-voltage probe. (A and B) Probe compensation can be either at the tip or at the end of the cable. (C) The correction box contains components to increase the bandwidth of the probe.

Figure 4.5 shows some arrangements of 10:1 probes. In Fig. 4.5A the indications of C, R_{in}, and C_{in} are the same as in Fig. 4.3. Additionally, it will be observed in Fig. 4.5C that for high-frequency probes the compensation network is not as simple as that in Fig. 4.3. This is due to the fact that the coaxial cable must be considered as a transmission line, which must be terminated with its characteristic impedance at the oscilloscope end. Otherwise, double reflections to the probe tip and back would occur and disturb the signal displayed on the screen. Thus a frequency-independent 10:1 divider is no longer attainable without extra components.

However, it appears to be impossible to match the characteristic impedance for *all* frequencies. Therefore, the lossy cable is introduced as an extra component. This means that the inner lead of the coaxial cable has been given a certain resistance, by using resistance wire. An advantage of the lossy cable is that any reflections will be damped, resulting in less disturbance of the signal to the oscilloscope.

Another detail to be taken into consideration while operating at high frequencies is the ground lead of the probe tip, because here the self-inductance of this lead becomes noticeable. For this reason special earth connectors can be attached to the probe tip. In Fig. 4.6 a passive 10 : 1 probe is shown with its accompanying accessories.

The influence of a long ground lead on the signal can be demonstrated by displaying a fast transient. Then, after each transient a damped oscillation known as *ringing* might occur (illustrated in Fig. 4.7).

Altogether the 10 : 1 probes show an input capacitance of about 10 to

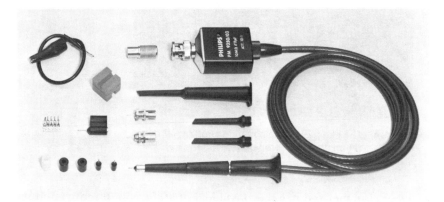

Fig. 4.6 A general-purpose 10 : 1 probe shown with its accessories.

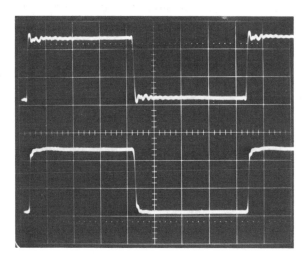

Fig. 4.7 The ringing in the upper trace is the effect of measuring with a probe having a ground connection. The use of a proper BNC adapter with the same probe results in the correct pulse shape being displayed (lower trace). Time-base speed is 50 ns/div.

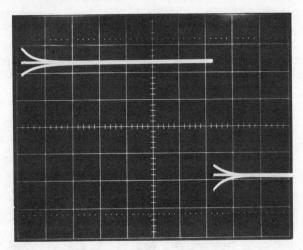

Fig. 4.8 The effect of probe compensation: a flat pulse is an indication that the proper adjustment has been made.

11 pF. Further reduction is possible, but at the cost of more attenuation. A 100:1 probe, such as the Philips PM 9358, shows an input capacitance of only 2 pF, the input resistance being 20 MΩ. Considering the 2 pF input capacitance, it can be easily understood that the ringing effect is also drastically reduced compared to the 10:1 probes. The ringing effect is shifted to a much higher frequency.

Another application for passive 100:1 probes is, of course, the measurement of high voltages (up to 5.6 kV ac peak-to-peak). This voltage is derated for frequencies above 1 MHz.

The frequency bandpass of both the 10:1 and the 100:1 probes is about 300 MHz. But the 100:1 probe should be used whenever the signal amplitude allows it, because of the 2-pF input capacitance. For example, a 5-V TTL pulse is reduced to 50 mV, but with an oscilloscope setting of 10 mV/div, this means a display of 5 divisions.

As already mentioned, the input (stray) capacitance is not the same for all oscilloscopes. For this the probe must be adjusted for optimum signal transfer. This adjustment should be made each time a probe is connected to another oscilloscope. For this adjustment most oscilloscopes are provided with a calibration generator, the output of which is available at the front panel and identified CAL. The calibration generator provides a square-wave output voltage at about 1 kHz. When the probe tip is connected to the CAL terminal, the operator can equalize the probe attenuation for high frequencies by means of a screwdriver adjustment of the trimmer capacitors shown in Fig. 4.5A, B, and C. The adjustment should be made until a flat square wave is obtained (see Fig. 4.8).

Terminated HF Probes

In the preceding paragraphs the importance of low input capacitances at the probe tip was stressed. However, at higher frequencies the input capacitance has much less impedance (X_c) than the 10- or 20-MΩ input resistance of the probe. For the circuit under test this means that as long as the internal source impedance is high, low input capacitance of the probe is important indeed. But in hf techniques very often low source impedances of 50 to 75 Ω are met and a normal 50-Ω coaxial cable can be used as the probe, provided that the cable is terminated with its characteristic impedance at the oscilloscope end. For an oscilloscope with an input impedance of 1 MΩ in parallel with 20 pF this means that a 50-Ω termination resistor is to be connected to its input terminals. Special hf oscilloscopes already have a 50-Ω input impedance.

If the cable load is too heavy, a 10 : 1 probe is available as a "terminated HF probe." The 10 : 1 attenuation is obtained by mounting a 450-Ω series resistor in the probe tip (see Fig. 4.9). The Philips 10 : 1 probe, PM 9342, for example, offers a 500-Ω loading in parallel with 0.7 pF and possesses a bandwidth of 3.5 GHz. The Philips 100 : 1 probe, PM 9343, has a 4950-Ω series resistor in the probe tip, thus showing an input resistance of 5000 Ω. The parallel capacitance in this case is 0.6 pF and the bandwidth is 1.7 GHz.

DC loading of the terminated hf probes can be eliminated by means of a blocking capacitor, normally supplied as an accessory to the probes.

Figure 4.10 shows a selection of passive-voltage probes from the Philips range.

4.3 ACTIVE-VOLTAGE PROBES (FET PROBES)

Thus far it has been established that, with normal passive-voltage probes, low-capacitive loading can only be obtained by means of high attenuation. The terminated hf probes offer better characteristics, but because of the heavy resistance loading they can only be used for low-impedance sources. The active-voltage probe (FET) was developed to overcome both of these disadvantages. Table 4.1 shows that the Philips probe PM 9353 has a load at its tip of only 3.5 pF in parallel with 1 MΩ at 1 : 1 attenuation. An even further reduction in capacitive loading can be

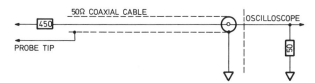

Fig. 4.9 Circuit diagram of terminated hf probe (10 : 1)

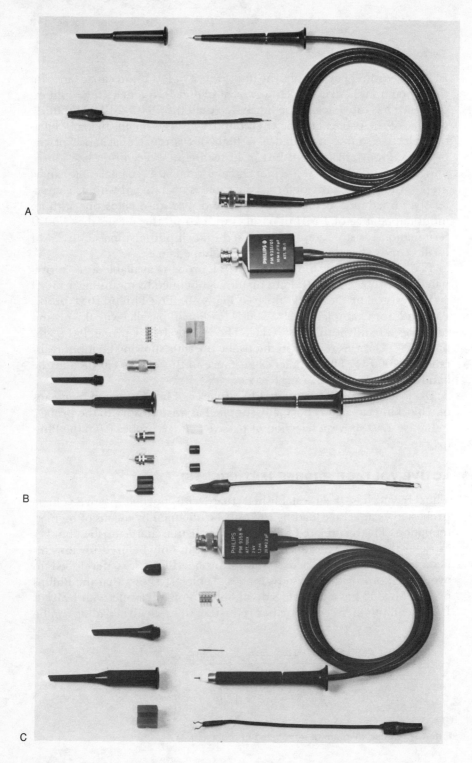

Fig. 4.10 A selection of passive-voltage probes from the Philips range.

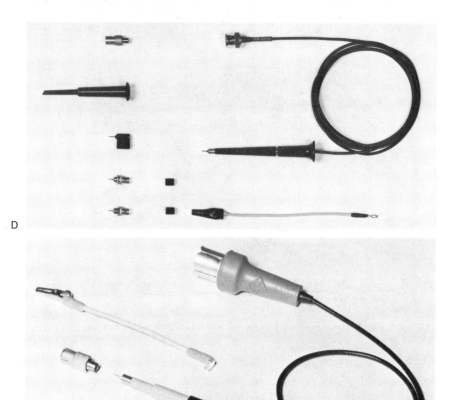

D

E

Fig. 4.10 (*Continued*)

Table 4.1

Probe type no.	Input RC (MΩ ‖ pF)	Attenuation (X)	Oscilloscope input	Bandwidth
Philips PM 9353	1 ‖ 3.5	1		220 MHz
	1 ‖ 2	10	1 MΩ ‖ 120 pF	220 MHz
	1 ‖ 1.5	100		220 MHz
Philips PM 9354	1 ‖ 3.5	2		1 GHz
	1 ‖ 2.8	10	50 Ω	1 GHz
	1 ‖ 1.8	50		1 GHz
	1 ‖ 1.4	100		1 GHz

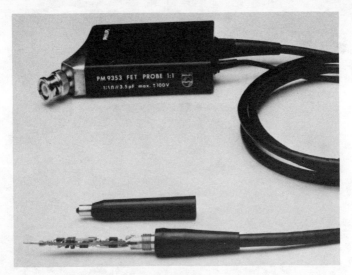

Fig. 4.11 A miniature FET input amplifier is built into the tip of the FET probe.

obtained by means of slip-on attenuators. Such probes make use of active circuitry to achieve their favorable characteristics.

Active-voltage probes obtain their power either from the oscilloscope-probe power supply (available at the oscilloscope front panel) or from a separate power unit (probe accessory).

To keep the probe small and easy to handle, a miniaturized amplifier is built into the tip of the probe (see Fig. 4.11). The input stage comprises a FET, which provides the high input impedance. Miniaturization results also in very small stray capacitances on the order of 3 to 4 pF. The amplification of the FET amplifier is adjusted exactly to 1, so no reduction in sensitivity occurs. Some considerations in the setup of FET probes are given in the following paragraphs.

A simplified block diagram is illustrated in Fig. 4.12. Here the amplification of the ac and dc signal components is separated and the components are combined again. In this way optimum use can be made of the characteristics of special transistors and integrated operational amplifiers. For example, in the dc path, lf transistors with a good $1/f$ noise figure and low drift can be used, while in the ac path special hf transistors are used. This principle is known as a *split-band amplifier*. The dc component is fed to one input terminal of a differential amplifier with gain factor A. As the other terminal of this amplifier is grounded, the former becomes virtually grounded also. In this way the input impedance is determined by R_1, and $R_1 = 1$ MΩ standard.

To keep the output signal exactly equal to the input signal, the output signal is compared with the input signal via a feedback inverter and re-sistor R_2. The value of R_2 depends upon the amplification factor of the inverter. If the latter is the same as that of the hf amplifier, then $R_2 = R_1$. In this way the difference between the input and output signals appears at the summing point S (Fig. 4.12). This difference is amplified by the differential amplifier and fed back to the output. The higher the amplification factor of the differential amplifier, the smaller the differ-ence between the input and output signals.

Summarizing, by means of this circuit the dc drift and the $1/f$ noise in the ac-coupled hf amplifier will be strongly reduced. Components of the signal which are cut off by the capacitor (dc component and lf part of the signal) appear as a difference between the input and output at summing point S; thus these components also will be restored by the differential amplifier. Consequently, a dc-coupled hf amplifier is the result.

Still, the necessity for ac coupling remains because it is frequently nec-essary to display a small ac signal superimposed on a high dc voltage. For this, capacitor C_1 may be switched into circuit, in series with R_1 (see Fig. 4.13). The signal at point S will be averaged to zero so that no dc level on the signal will be present at the output. This gives the same result as the inclusion of a capacitor in series with the input. The advantage of this method of ac coupling is that C_1 *is not directly coupled with the hf path* but via R_1, so that the switch in parallel with C_1 will not affect the hf bandpass properties of the probe due to its stray capacitances.

Figure 4.13 also differs from Fig. 4.12 in that a dc voltage can be ap-plied to the input terminal of the differential amplifier that was con-nected to ground in Fig. 4.12. Compensation for a dc voltage level pres-ent in the signal is obtained in this way, while the dc coupling of the

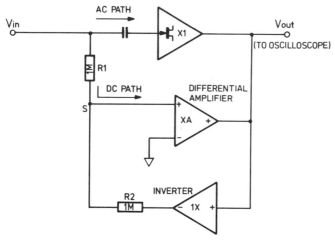

Fig. 4.12 Simplified block diagram of a FET probe.

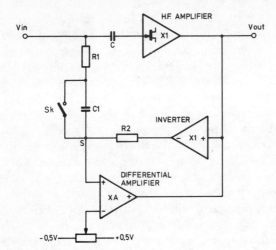

Fig. 4.13 Block diagram of a FET probe.

signal is still possible. This example of an active-voltage probe applies to the Philips FET probe PM 9353.

Note When applying a FET probe, it should never be forgotten that the justification for using an active probe is to obtain a high input impedance, that is, high resistance and low capacitance. This makes it possible to measure high frequencies without a reduction in sensitivity, in other words, to measure *millivolts above 25 MHz*.

Slip-on attenuators can be attached to the probe tip. These attenuators contain a resistor divider of 10:1 or 100:1. Therefore, the input resistance remains 1 MΩ, but the capacitances become 2.5 and 1.5 pF, respectively. Thus the capacitive loading is even less compared with the normal 1:1 FET probe. However, this is achieved at the cost of 10× and 100× attenuation.

Summary

When connecting a probe tip to a measuring circuit, it should not be overlooked that part of the signal is taken off from the circuit. Consequently, the circuit is influenced in its behavior by the load of the probe.

The graph in Fig. 4.14 gives some typical examples. This frequency dependence is primarily caused by the cable impedance (compare with Fig. 4.5). The parallel impedances X_p and R_p in Fig. 4.14 are in fact the calculated equivalents of the entire probe networks. Similarly, the equivalent input resistance is frequency-dependent. The X_p and R_p curves are given in the probe documentation. The FET probe is best suited for very sensitive high-frequency measurements. For very high frequencies the

terminated hf probe is a good solution, provided that the source impedance of the circuit under test is low and the signal is not too small.

4.4 CURRENT PROBES

Basically, the current probe is a transformer of which the primary winding is the test lead through which the current is measured (see Fig. 4.15).
The probe head consists of a ferrox-cube core and the secondary windings of the transformer. The core can be split into two parts in order to
clip it simply around the measuring lead. The white-colored part of the
probe head (Fig. 4.16) can be moved backwards and forwards to clip it
around the lead. A voltage is developed in the transformer secondary

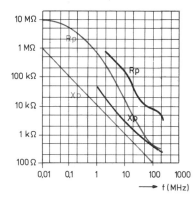

Fig. 4.14 X_p and R_p curves of a 10:1 passive-
voltage probe (grey) and a FET probe (black).
An improvement in the FET probe's loading effect at high frequencies can be seen.

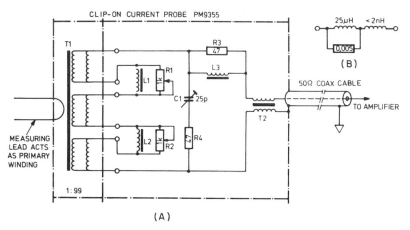

(A)

Fig. 4.15 Circuit diagram of current probe head. (A) R_1, R_2, and C_1 are adjustable for optimum pulse response. $R_3 \parallel L_3$ and T_2 together compensate losses in the
50-Ω coaxial cable. (B) Equivalent circuit showing the impedance inserted into the
lead by the probe.

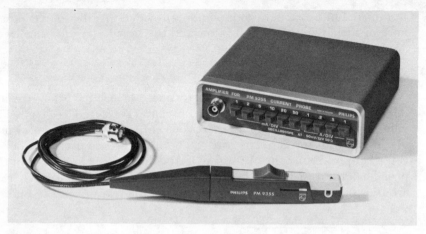

Fig. 4.16 Active-current probe provides calibrated deflection on the oscilloscope screen ranging from 1 mA/div to 1 A/div.

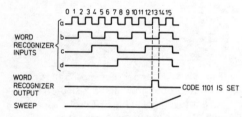

Fig. 4.17 Timing diagram shows how the oscilloscope can be triggered from a unique combination of logic states, employing a word recognizer

windings by the magnetic field around the measuring lead. This voltage is fed to an amplifier box, the output of which is fed to the oscilloscope. The output cable from the amplifier must be terminated with 50 Ω at the oscilloscope end (low-ohmic system for 75-MHz bandwidth). Furthermore, if the oscilloscope is set to 50-mV/div sensitivity, the amplifier box provides calibrated outputs ranging from 1 mA/div on the screen.

Applications for current probes include:

• Switching currents in power supplies, turn-on and turn-off currents of systems, transistors, and silicon controlled rectifiers (SCRs). The current probe may reveal more information about overload conditions than voltage transients do.

• Circuits where minimum loading by the measuring device is necessary. The current probe only loads the lead under test between 0.5 and 2 pF, depending upon its diameter. For most applications the impedance inserted into the lead by the probe can be disregarded (see Fig. 4.15B).

• Current difference. This is achieved by feeding two leads through the probe head such that the currents flow in opposite directions. The difference between the currents is measured at a very high rejection rate for currents that are common mode. Sensitivity can be increased simply by feeding more turns of wire through the clip-on head. The upper range can be extended by splitting the current path into a number of parallel wires and feeding only one current path through the probe head.

4.5 LOGIC TRIGGER PROBE

In the more sophisticated digital practice, it frequently happens that the engineer wants to trigger an oscilloscope on a particular word or combination of bits (simultaneously) present at a number of lines, for example, in a BCD parallel output of a frequency counter. Word recognizers, suitable for use in conjunction with oscilloscopes, are readily available as a kind of probe. Usually they have a number of inputs complying with tetrad or octad length (4 or 8). A binary word can be set by switches, and if this word is detected, the unit initiates a trigger which can be used to start a sweep. Alternatively, the trigger can be used to initiate a sweep after a certain delay time by making use of the digital or analog delayed-sweep facility. In this way the display can be started on a recognizable byte, character, or any unique combination of data in logic circuits. For example, the start of the display can be made to coincide with a control byte coming from a peripheral or a BCD output of a decade counter. An example of this is illustrated in Fig. 4.17.

4.6 EXERCISES

For each exercise, circle the answer you believe is correct.

1. A 10:1 probe has an advantage over a 1:1 passive-voltage probe because:

    (A) It has a lower input capacitance.

    (B) It has a higher bandwidth.

    (C) Higher voltages can be measured.

2. Terminated hf probes and active FET probes both offer low-capacitive loading. However, the FET probe is preferred because it causes:

    (A) Less attenuation

    (B) Less resistive loading

    (C) Both A and B

3. FET probes are mainly used to:

(A) Measure FET transistors

(B) Block dc voltages

(C) Measure low voltages at high frequencies

4. Current probes may be used for:

(A) Feeding a current into a circuit

(B) Measuring currents through leads

(C) Measuring currents on printed circuit boards

MEASUREMENT PITFALLS

5.1 INTRODUCTION

In this chapter, the ways that measuring results may be misleading or misunderstood are pointed out. These problems can be caused by incorrect connections between the device under test and the oscilloscope. Also, the limited capabilities of the oscilloscope itself may cause misreadings. As the knowledge of the amplification of pulse-shaped waveforms is of paramount importance for this subject, the definitions and some theory are treated to begin with in this chapter.

5.2 PULSE DEFINITIONS

Observation of pulses is one of the most frequent applications of an oscilloscope. An "ideal" pulse-shaped waveform is shown in Fig. 5.1.

During a certain time $(t_0 - t_1)$ the voltage v is at a predetermined level v_0. Then, at instant t_1, a level step takes place from v_0 to v_1. This level is maintained until t_2, when a step back to v_0 takes place. At t_3 this is repeated. Because the transitions in the levels take no time, the pulse in Fig. 5.1 is "ideal." Both levels v_0 and v_1 remain constant during the time intervals. In practice "ideal" pulses do not exist. Some aberrations of the "ideal" waveform are given in Fig. 5.2 with the related nomenclature.

In Fig. 5.2 the 0% level is not the 0-V level. The difference is called *dc-offset*. The rising slope does not start immediately but gradually via a *rounding* (just below the 10% level). The same kind of roundings are present anywhere a change in level starts. Furthermore, it takes a finite time for the transition to reach the other level (up or down). Due to the roundings the *rise time t_r* and *fall time t_f* of the pulse are defined between the 10% and 90% levels (see Fig. 5.2). Between these two levels the slopes are, in practice, usually rather straight and determination of t_r and t_f is possible now, which is not the case between the 0% and 100% levels. Sometimes the 20% and 80% levels are chosen for t_r and t_f, but in those cases it is mentioned explicitly. When nothing additional to t_r and t_f is specified, the 10% and 90% levels are meant. From Fig. 5.2 it is clear that t_r and t_f are different, which in general they are.

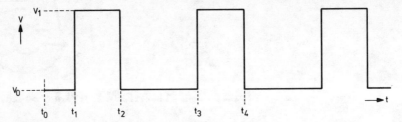

Fig. 5.1 "Ideal" pulse-shaped waveform.

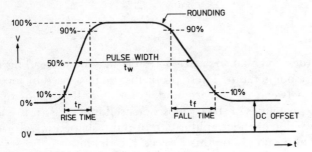

Fig. 5.2 Aberrations of an ideal pulse waveform.

In Fig. 5.2 the pulse duration or pulse width t_w is not constant at all voltage levels between 0% and 100%. For this reason the pulse width is always measured at the 50% level.

Figure 5.3 shows more pulse aberrations. Sometimes before the upgoing slope starts, a little downgoing *preshoot* can be noticed. This can be caused, for example, in an inverting amplifier stage, by the stray capacitances between input and output. At the end of the upgoing slope the voltage rises too high, which is called *overshoot*. For the downgoing slope this is sometimes called *undershoot*. Sometimes the pulse comes along with *ringing;* this effect was illustrated in Fig. 4.7. Due to capacitive coupling between amplifier stages, the voltage level may not remain constant but show a *droop*. The similar effect may be caused by temperature changes in the amplifier output stages.

Note: For pulses as in Fig. 5.3 it may be difficult to determine t_r and t_f. The practice is first to display a number of pulses per division on the screen and determine the average 0% and 100% amplitudes, after which t_r and t_f can be measured.

Finally, some timing notations with respect to pulses are given in Fig. 5.4. The time between two successive pulses is the *pulse space*. For repetitive pulse signals a *repetition time* t_{rep} may be defined. Figure 5.4 is a simple example; other repetition times are shown in Fig. 1.9.

In a simple pulse train as shown in Fig. 5.4, a *duty cycle* may be defined as the ratio of the pulse-width time t_w and the repetition time t_{rep}. It denotes the part of the period that the pulse is in duty. If the duty cycle is $\frac{1}{2}$, one may speak of a *square wave,* assuming that $t_r = t_f \ll t_{\text{rep}}$. For example, a square wave exists if, in Fig. 5.1, the period $t_1 - t_2$ equals $t_2 - t_3$, etc.

In digital techniques it can happen that two pulses appear in a time-related sequence, but that the second pulse appears a little later, with a *delay,* with respect to the first one.

If in one signal the successive pulses do not have exactly the same repetition time, it is said that the signal has *jitter* (see also Fig. 2.28*A*).

5.3 BANDWIDTH VERSUS RISE TIME ($B\tau_r = 0.35$)

As will be explained in Sec. 7.4, Note 7.1, the bandwidth denotes one of the characteristics of an amplifier and the phase another characteristic. The effect of both can be studied by applying an "ideal" square-wave pulse to the input of the amplifier and studying the output voltage.

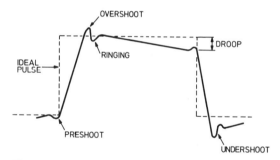

Fig. 5.3 Detail of aberrations of an ideal pulse waveform.

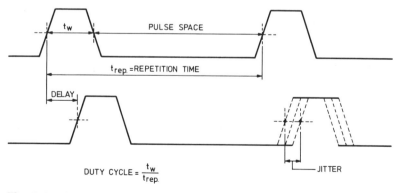

Fig. 5.4 Timing definitions of pulses.

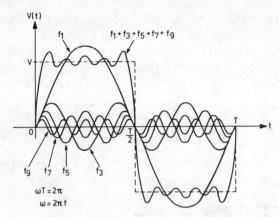

Fig. 5.5 A pulse can be composed from a series (infinite) of sine waves.

This can be understood if one considers the square wave as being composed of a series (infinite) of sine waves. For example, refer to Fig. 5.5, where a pulse is approximated by 5 harmonics, each with its own amplitude and mutual phase. For an exact replica of the waveform, infinite harmonics are needed. The formula for the waveform in Fig. 5.5 is given by the Fourier analysis

$$V(t) = \frac{4V}{\pi} (\sin \omega t + \tfrac{1}{3} \sin 3\omega t + \tfrac{1}{5} \sin 5\omega t + \cdots)$$

After amplification with a factor A, the output voltage $V_0(t)$ will be

$$V_0(t) = A \cdot \frac{4V}{\pi} (\sin \omega t + \tfrac{1}{3} \sin 3\omega t + \tfrac{1}{5} \sin 5\omega t + \cdots)$$

If the amplifier is not ideal, but has an amplitude characteristic as, for example, the line of dashes in Fig. 7.3, the n harmonics are not amplified by a factor A, but every one is amplified by a different factor A_n. The expression for the output voltage $V_0(t)$ will be

$$V_0(t) = \frac{4V}{\pi} (A_1 \sin \omega t + A_3 \sin 3\omega t + A_5 \sin 5\omega t + \cdots)$$

If, in addition, the phase characteristic of the amplifier is not ideal, then each harmonic reaches the output with a different phase shift and the total result will be

$$V_0(t) = \frac{4V}{\pi} [A_1 \sin (\omega t + \varphi_1) + A_3 \sin (3\omega t + \varphi_3)$$
$$+ A_5 \sin (5\omega t + \varphi_5) + \cdots]$$

It will be clear that due to this behavior of the amplifier the "ideal" *input* square wave appears distorted at the output. For example, the rise time τ_r is not 0 but has a certain value (see Fig. 5.5). The more harmonics are amplified "linearly" (in the right way: same amplification factor and phase shift), the better the result and the shorter the rise time τ_r at the output. The value of τ_r depends on the frequency of the harmonics, which are of course determined by the frequency of the square wave.

It can thus be stated that the shorter the rise time τ_r of the output pulse as a response to an ideal input pulse, the more harmonics are amplified linearly and the higher the bandwidth B of the amplifier (see Fig. 7.1). It can be shown that for an amplifier with a bandwidth B, the rise time τ_r is related to it according to

$$B\tau_r = 0.35$$

where B = bandwidth, Hz
$\quad \tau_r$ = rise time, s

Example: For the Philips 50-MHz oscilloscope PM 3240, as discussed in Sec. 7.3, the rise time is

$$\tau_r = \frac{0.35}{50 \times 10^6 \text{ s}}$$
$$= 7 \text{ ns}$$

This oscilloscope thus shows a 7-ns rise time as a response to an "ideal" input square wave. As a matter of fact, this is the way the oscilloscope is tested. A pulse for which $\tau_r \ll 7$ ns [for example, $\tau_r = 100$ ps ($= 10^{-10}$ s)], is applied to the input, and the rise time is measured from the screen.

5.4 CALCULATION OF RISE TIMES

After the previous paragraphs have been studied, the following question may now arise:

What will be the overall rise time if a couple of amplifiers, each having a certain rise time, are connected in cascade (one output to next input)?

The exact behavior of such an amplifier chain can be calculated and many examples were computed. For the overall rise time very often no simple expression can be derived and tables or curves were drawn after computation. Although exact expressions can be calculated, an empirical formula is derived which approximates the result of all computations:

$$\tau_{rN} = \sqrt{\tau_{r1}^2 + \tau_{r2}^2 + \tau_{r3}^2 + \cdots + \tau_{rn}^2}$$

where τ_{rN} = the overall rise time of the amplifier chain
$\quad \tau_{rn}$ = the rise time of each of the n amplifier stages

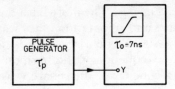

Fig. 5.6 Basic setup for rise-time measurements.

The meaning of this result is explained with the aid of some examples.

The oscilloscope illustrated in Fig. 5.6 has a rise time of $\tau_0 = 7$ ns. An impulse of $\tau_p = 0.5$ ns is fed to the oscilloscope.

Question 1: What will be the result on the screen (τ_s)?

Answer: The total result will be

$$\tau_s^2 = \tau_p^2 + \tau_0^2$$
$$= 0.25 + 49$$
$$\tau_s = \sqrt{49.25}$$
$$= 7.07 \text{ ns}$$
$$\approx 7 \text{ ns} = \tau_0$$

Thus, the only thing seen on the screen is the rise time of the oscilloscope itself.

Note: In fact the rise time of an oscilloscope is determined in this way, thus feeding it with an impulse with a short rise time with respect to the (expected) rise time of the oscilloscope.

Question 2: What will be the result on the screen in Fig. 5.6 if $\tau_p = 7$ ns?

Answer: $\tau_s = \sqrt{\tau_p^2 + \tau_0^2}$
$$= 9.90 \text{ ns}$$

Thus, instead of the expected 7 ns, the oscilloscope displays 10 ns, owing to the rise time of the oscilloscope's vertical system.

Note: Here again the practice is reversed. Displayed on the screen is $\tau_s = 10$ ns, and *we know* that for our oscilloscope $\tau_0 = 7$ ns. Hence, the impulse to be measured has a rise time of

$$\tau_p = \sqrt{\tau_s^2 - \tau_0^2}$$
$$= 7 \text{ ns}$$

Question 3: What will be the rise time of an impulse if the display on the screen shows 50 ns? $\tau_0 = 7$ ns.

Answer: $\tau_p^2 = \tau_s^2 - \tau_0^2$

$$= 2500 - 49 = 3564$$

$$\tau_p = 49.5 \text{ ms} \approx \tau_s$$

So in this case, where $\tau_p \gg \tau_0$, the display can be considered the correct answer.

Accuracy of Rise-Time Measurements

As we have seen in Sec. 5.3, the oscilloscope used for the above calculations had a 50-MHz bandwidth, such as the Philips PM 3240. The maximum time-base coefficient is 50 ns/div, while a time-base magnifier of $5\times$ is provided as well, resulting in a maximum time coefficient of 10 ns/div. The time-base coefficient error of the PM 3240 is specified as $\pm 3\%$ (Chap. 7), and the additional error of the time-base magnifier is $\pm 2\%$, together resulting in an overall error of $\pm 5\%$.

Refer to the calculations in questions 1 and 3. In question 3 the mathematical error is 1%. Furthermore, the maximum time coefficient is 10 ns/div; thus the oscilloscope's own rise time is shown as 0.7 division ($=0.7$ cm). From the screen a 1% deviation of 0.7 cm cannot be read, while the 5% time coefficient error is over ruling the calculated 1%. Even a 3-ns pulse would lead to a calculated display of 7.62 ns, which would read 7 ns from the screen (0.762). A 4-ns pulse leads to a reading of 8.06 ns on the screen. From this it will be clear that, in order to determine the rise time of an oscilloscope, a pulse rise time is needed which is only 2 to 3 times shorter than the expected rise time of the oscilloscope.

For the same reasons it can be stated that rise-time measurements from the screen (as shown in question 3) can be performed without the mathematical corrections for rise times which are about 2 to 3 times longer than the oscilloscope's rise time. For example, in question 3, a 20-ns pulse would lead to a calculated display of 21.19 ns, resulting in a display of 2.1 divisions ($=2.1$ cm).

Without mathematical correction there is an error of 5%, which is on the same order as the time coefficient error in the magnified mode.

Note that due to the latter error the display could deviate from 2.0 to 2.2 divisions (20 ns or 22 ns). Indeed, if the mathematical corrections were made, the results would deviate from 18.73 to 20.86 ns, or an error of -6 to $+4\%$ with respect to 20 ns.

A 35-ns pulse at the input would lead to a calculated display of 35.69 ns, or 3.7 divisions, which cannot be distinguished from 3.5 divisions in practice. In this case only the time-base coefficient error is of importance.

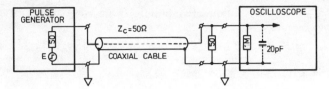

Fig. 5.7 Correct cable termination for measuring with a high-input-impedance oscilloscope.

5.5 CABLE TERMINATION WITH PULSE MEASUREMENTS

As already explained in Sec. 5.3, a pulse-shaped waveform contains a great number of high harmonics. If a pulse waveform is to be studied from the screen, the pulses have to be transported from the signal source to the oscilloscope. If a cable is used for the transport, all harmonics of the pulses must pass along the cable. In fact, the cable acts as a transmission line, which means that the transmission-line theory is valid. From this theory, it follows that for an optimum power transport the cable's characteristic impedance Z_c must match the signal source's internal impedance Z_i and that the cable is terminated at the far end by its characteristic impedance. For example, for an ordinary coaxial cable (RG 58U), $Z_c = 50\Omega$, and in practice most pulse generators also possess an internal impedance of $Z_i = 50\Omega$.

The correct way to connect a pulse generator to an oscilloscope is illustrated by Fig. 5.7 for an oscilloscope with a standard 1 MΩ ∥ 20 pF input impedance. A 50-Ω termination resistor is connected externally in parallel with oscilloscope input.

Against this simple rule two mistakes are frequently made.

1. At the oscilloscope side the cable is not terminated, except by the oscilloscope's input impedance, 1 MΩ ∥ 20 pF.

2. At the pulse-generator side ($Z_i = 50\ \Omega$), an extra 50-Ω termination resistor is connected in parallel with the 50-Ω cable, while no cable termination is provided at the oscilloscope side (only 1 MΩ ∥ 20 pF). See Fig. 5.10.

The results can be studied from the photograph in Fig. 5.8. The upper trace shows the result of mistake 1, the middle trace shows the result of mistake 2, and the lower trace shows the correct result with termination according to Fig. 5.7. Figure 5.8 is a multiple-exposure photograph with the same settings of the pulse generator and oscilloscope for all traces, except that before each exposure the trace is shifted slightly with the Y POSITION control knob.

The amplitude of the upper trace is twice that of the lower trace. This is because the oscilloscope's input impedance means virtually an open end to the cable. Here no current flows and the open emf of the pulse generator is measured. The explanation of this is in Fig. 5.9.

The cable in this figure causes a propagation delay of 5 ns, meaning that the signal from the pulse generator needs 5 ns to reach the oscillo-

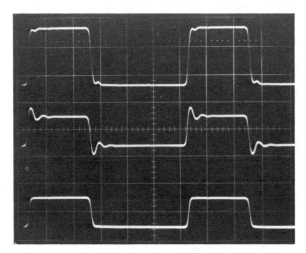

Fig. 5.8 The effects of various cable terminations are demonstrated in this multi-exposure picture. (Upper trace) No termination at the oscilloscope side. (Center trace) Extra 50-Ω resistor at the pulse generator side and no termination at the oscilloscope side. (Lower trace) Correct termination at the oscilloscope side.

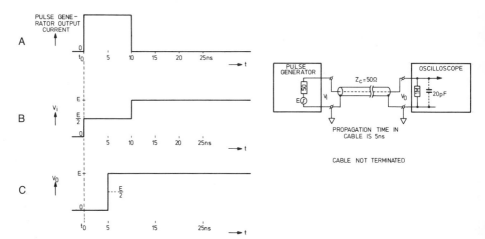

Fig. 5.9 Pulse waveforms for a virtually open-ended connection at the oscilloscope side.

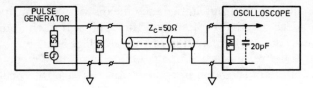

Fig. 5.10 Incorrect termination at the pulse generator side will result in the center trace shown in Fig. 5.8.

scope. If at t_0 the voltage of the pulse generator (PG) goes high, then as long as the transient propagates through the cable, the PG is terminated with the 50 Ω of the cable impedance, the output current is nominal, and the output voltage is half the emf of the PG ($E/2$, see Fig. 5.9B). Then, after 5 ns the signal reaches the virtually open end at the oscilloscope side. Therefore, the signal will be reflected and the amplitude is doubled at that point. This is also the voltage that is measured and displayed on the screen (Fig. 5.9C). Again, 5 ns later (10 ns after t_0), the reflection reaches the PG, causing a drop in the output current. The PG "knows" now that no current is needed. The aberration at the beginning of the pulse is caused by a small reflection at the oscilloscope side. The reflections are absorbed by the pulse generator ($Z_i = 50$ Ω).

In Fig. 5.8 the time-base setting of the oscilloscope was 50 ns/div. The cable used (RG 58U) was about 1 m long, providing about 5-ns propagation time.

Figure 5.10 shows the wrong connection mentioned as mistake 2, the result being the middle trace in Fig 5.8.

Note that the voltage rises in the first instance above the final value $E/2$. When at t_0 the voltage of the PG goes high, the 50-Ω termination resistor is in parallel with the 50-Ω cable impedance, resulting in a total of 25 Ω. Thus, in the first instance only $E/3$ is transmitted towards the oscilloscope, at which point the reflection causes it to rise to $2E/3$, which is above $E/2$. Also, the reflection meets 25 Ω at the PG side, now causing a decrement instead of an increment. This action is also repeated and can be observed more clearly in the photograph than the action in the upper trace.

The lower trace in Fig. 5.8 is the correct result. If the output voltage of the PG goes high, the PG is loaded with the 50-Ω cable impedance. After 5 ns the signal reaches the 50-Ω termination resistor, in which it will be dissipated without causing reflections. This voltage is measured by the oscilloscope. The transmission-line theory applies equally of course for signals other than pulses. For example, if high-frequency TV signals are to be displayed, a 75-Ω TV cable must be terminated with 75 Ω at the oscilloscope side.

5.6 CONSEQUENCES OF WRONG-PROBE ADJUSTMENTS

Section 4.2 discussed probe adjustment for good frequency response when using a probe-oscilloscope combination (see Fig. 4.8). In Figs. 5.11, 5.12, and 5.13 three possible adjustments of the probe's compensation network are shown. The upper trace in Fig. 5.11 shows the correct probe compensation; flat square waves of about 2 kHz are obtained. The lower

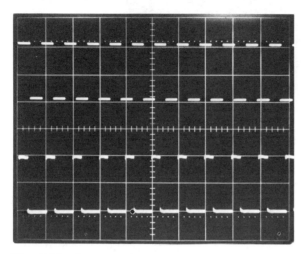

Fig. 5.11 Correct probe adjustment (upper trace) results in a 1-MHz pulse display of 2 divisions (lower trace).

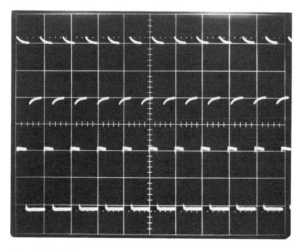

Fig. 5.12 Overcompensation of the probe (upper trace) results in a 1-MHz pulse display of more than 2 divisions (lower trace).

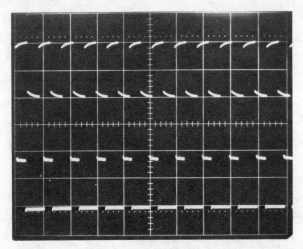

Fig. 5.13 Undercompensation of the probe (upper trace) results in a 1-MHz pulse display of less than 2 divisions (lower trace).

trace shows a 1-MHz pulse (double-exposure photographs) with an amplitude of 2 divisions. Figure 5.12 shows overcompensation in the upper trace; thus the higher frequencies are extra-amplified (compare Figs. 7.3 and 7.4). As the frequency of the 1-MHz pulses is much higher than the calibration square wave of about 2 kHz, the amplitudes of the 1 MHz pulses are displayed too high (in this case more than 2 divisions). Figure 5.13 shows the case of undercompensation, resulting in amplitudes of the 1-MHz pulses that are too low (less than 2 divisions).

The probe-oscilloscope combination used for this example has led to amplitudes of the 1-MHz pulses in Figs. 5.11 and 5.13 of 2.1 and 1.6 divisions, respectively. The difference is 0.5 division; for a 2-division pulse, this means a measuring *deviation of 25%*. This is one order of magnitude more than the scope accuracy of 2 to 3% due only to a wrong probe adjustment!

Note: This statement is of course not only valid for pulses, but also for sine waves and other waveforms. A misalignment of the probe to the oscilloscope input may lead to wrong amplitude measurements.

5.7 MEASUREMENTS AT THE UPPER FREQUENCY LIMIT OF THE SCOPE

Another source of erroneous amplitude measurement, other than a wrong probe adjustment, may be the limitation in bandwidth of the oscilloscope. Most oscilloscopes possess a frequency characteristic shaped as the solid line in Fig. 7.3.

It must be realized, however, that this illustration means that at the upper limits the signal is amplified 3 dB less (or about -30%!) than the lower-frequency signals (for example, 50 kHz). Figure 5.14 shows in one photograph (double-exposed) the upper and lower traces, respectively, of a 10-MHz signal and a 50-kHz signal. The signal at the output of the generator remained constant in amplitude and the oscilloscope at the same attenuator setting. The 50-kHz signal has a peak-to-peak amplitude of 3 divisions, and the upper trace, 2.1 divisions. Obviously, the bandwidth of the oscilloscope in use is 10 MHz.

Note: The example given here is exact at the upper limit, but between 0 and -3 dB, the display decreases gradually with increasing frequency.

The limitations of the bandwidth become even worse when high-frequency pulses are displayed. Figure 5.15 shows in the upper trace the display of a 1-MHz square wave, again on a 10-MHz oscilloscope. The pulse generator's rise time was set at 2.4 ns; thus for the oscilloscope ($\tau_r = 35$ ns), this is almost an ideal pulse. As explained in example 1 in Sec. 5.4, the visible rise time in Fig. 5.15 is that of the oscilloscope itself (time-base setting was 0.5 μs/div).

Now if the frequency of the pulses is raised to 10 MHz—the lower trace in Fig. 5.15—almost all the higher-frequency harmonics are cut off by the frequency characteristic of the oscilloscope and only the first harmonic (sine wave) remains (compare again with Fig. 5.5). The result is

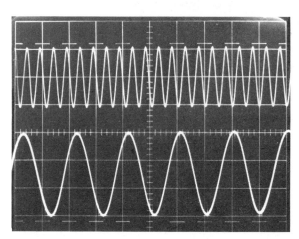

Fig. 5.14 Double exposure of 10 MHz (upper trace) and 50 kHz (lower trace) sine waves, both having the same amplitudes. Because of the 10-MHz bandwidth, the signal shown in the upper trace is amplified 3 dB less than that shown in the lower trace.

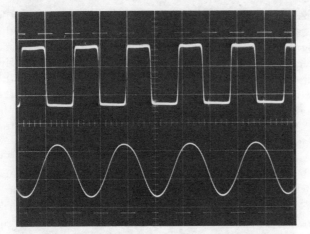

Fig. 5.15 Double exposure of a 1-MHz square wave (upper trace) and a 10-MHz square wave (lower trace) taken from the screen of a 10-MHz oscilloscope.

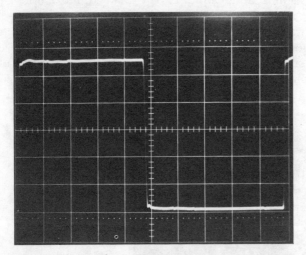

Fig. 5.16 The same 1-MHz square wave shown in the upper trace of Fig. 5.15 is displayed here on a 50-MHz oscilloscope.

given in the lower trace (time-base setting of 0.2 μs/div, magnifier $\times 5$). Indeed, a slightly distorted sine wave is displayed.

Figure 5.16 shows the same 1-MHz square wave (the upper trace in Fig. 5.15), but now displayed on a 50-MHz oscilloscope and with a time-base setting of 0.1 μs/div. The aberrations in the pulse also become more clear.

5.8 TIMING ERRORS WITH PULSE MEASUREMENTS

While measuring complex waveforms in digital techniques, mistakes can be made very easily. In this section examples of this are presented. Some of them are explained in detail, in order to gain knowledge about the possible reasons for false triggering, which leads to wrong timing displays on the screen.

Figure 5.17 shows the display of a square wave and a double pulse in the correct time relation. Now, if the main time base (MTB) is triggered with the lower trace signal, then in the alternate mode, the lower trace could be started with the first of the double pulses, and the upper trace with the second pulse.

The result may be as illustrated in Fig. 5.18, which shows a wrong time relation between the two signals. The chopped mode also could be used in this case, resulting in a vague, unstable picture that would indicate something is wrong. The way to avoid this is to trigger on the upper-trace signal, which has in each repetition time only one upgoing slope and one downgoing slope of the signals.

The following example is a little more complicated and the possible trigger errors are explained in more detail. Two pulse trains are generated, together with a square wave. Refer to Fig. 5.19, a photograph taken from a four-trace oscilloscope. The upper trace shows the square wave, while the middle and lower traces show the successive signals: a triple and double pulse, respectively. From now on the lower trace is

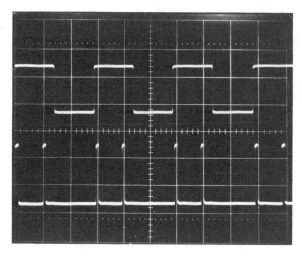

Fig. 5.17 Of these two time-related signals, the triggering of the signal shown in the upper trace results in a proper time relationship.

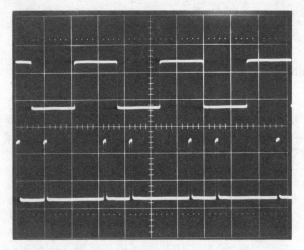

Fig. 5.18 The same signals shown in Fig. 5.17, but triggering here is at the lower-trace signal. An incorrect time relationship may be displayed.

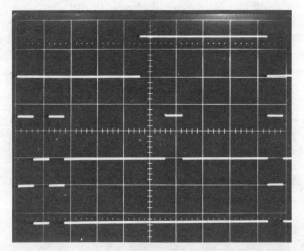

Fig. 5.19 In these three time-selected signals, triggering occurs at the negative slope of the signal in the upper trace. The time relationship is correct.

called *signal A*, the middle trace is *signal B*, and the upper trace *signal C*. In the illustration, triggering takes place at the negative slope of signal *C*.

Now suppose that only signal *A* and signal *B* are displayed and that the oscilloscope is *triggered at signal A*. Then, in the ALTERNATE mode, the result might be as shown in either Fig. 5.20 or 5.21, depending on the position of the electronic channel switch at the start of the first written trace. Thus, either signal A or signal B is written first, but *both displays show the wrong timing* (compare with Fig. 5.19).

This phenomenon is explained with the aid of Fig. 5.22. When in the alternate mode the trigger source is channel A, then the sweeps are started at pulse number 1 and pulse number 2 alternately. Now, if with the first sweep, signal A is displayed—this depends on the internal position of the electronic channel selector switch (Fig. 2.2)—then the display

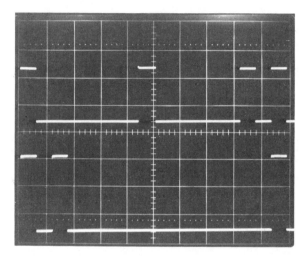

Fig. 5.20 Erroneous triggering results in a wrong time relationship, as shown by the display illustrated here.

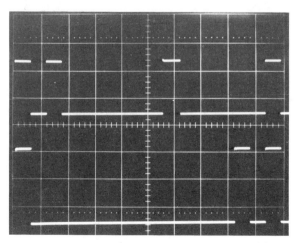

Fig. 5.21 A further example of incorrect time relationship due to erroneous triggering is shown here.

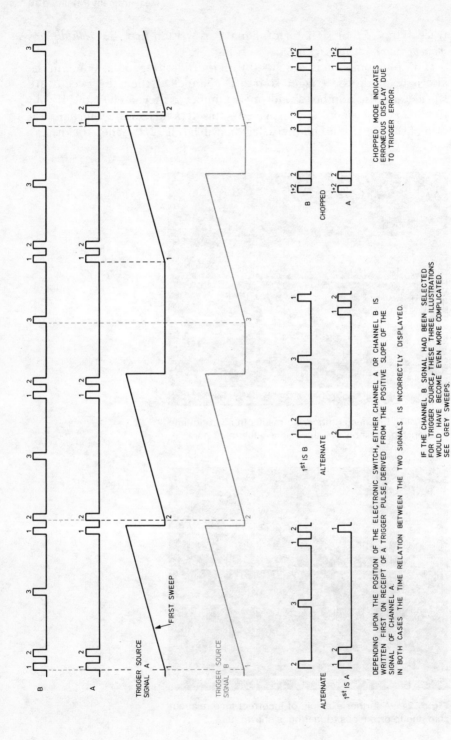

Fig. 5.22 Diagrammatic explanation for the incorrect time relationship shown in Figs. 5.20 and 5.21.

will be as shown in Fig. 5.20. The pulse indication numbers are given in Fig. 5.22. If the measuring procedure is started when channel B is displayed, then the result will be as shown in Fig. 5.21. In order to make sure that the display shows the correct time relation, the chopped mode can be used. Although this results in a wrong picture (Fig. 5.23), the operator will be sure that erroneous triggering takes place and that corrective measures can be taken. If available, the operator should use the signal shown in the upper trace in Fig. 5.19, either internally if a four-trace oscilloscope is available or externally if triggered with a dual-trace oscilloscope.

5.9 HUM ON SIGNALS

Very often hum is present on the signals under test. This can be easily determined from the screen, because the hum is related to the line frequency. If a signal shows a kind of unexpected amplitude modulation, switching back the time-base setting to about 5 to 10 or 20 ms/div, and switching over the trigger *source* selector to MAINS (or LINE), will generally result in a stable picture in the event of hum.

Figure 5.24 shows a 250-kHz square-wave signal whose amplitude is rather vague. Switching back the TIME/DIV to 5 ms/div and triggering from MAINS results in a stable display of a 20-ms envelope. This means that a 50-Hz hum is present on the square-wave signal (see Fig. 5.25).

Figure 5.26 is a photograph (double-exposed) of a case where the power supply of a pulse generator is defective. The lower trace shows the varying amplitudes of the pulses. Switching the oscilloscope to 5

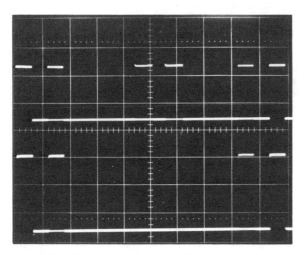

Fig. 5.23 The chopped mode indicates an erroneous display due to trigger error.

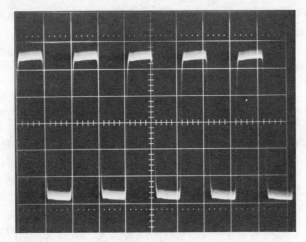

Fig. 5.24 The vague amplitude of a 250-kHz square wave indicates that something is wrong.

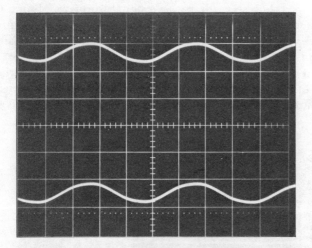

Fig. 5.25 The same 250-kHz square wave shown in Fig. 5.24 is displayed at 5 ms/div and with MAINS (line) triggering. The 4-cm sine wave envelope indicates the 50-Hz hum.

ms/div and MAINS triggering showed the cause of the trouble immediately, a 50-Hz dip in the output which can only be caused by the power supply of the pulse generator (upper trace).

5.10 AC-DC INPUT COUPLING WITH X-Y MEASUREMENTS

À pitfall sometimes met in *X-Y* measurements is different coupling of the input channels, for example, *X* via channel *A* is dc-coupled and *Y* via channel *B* is ac-coupled. In Sec. 2.1, the input coupling is discussed with possible consequences for *X-t* measurements.

In Chap. 7 the specification of the PM 3240 oscilloscope for ac-coupled input is stated by giving an "input RC time" of about 22 ms. With 1-MΩ input resistance this means a coupling capacitor of 22 nF. From this it follows that for 7.23 Hz a phase shift of 45° occurs ($1/2\pi fC = 10^6\ \Omega$) compared to a dc-coupled input. This must be borne in mind and avoided when operating the oscilloscope in the *X-Y* mode.

Figure 5.27 shows the *X-Y* display of a same sine-wave signal of 20 Hz. One channel is dc-coupled; the other ac-coupled. The fraction cut off the *Y* axis is arcsin φ, with φ being the phase shift between the *X* and *Y* signals. From the illustration can be read arcsin $\varphi \approx \frac{3}{8}$; so that $\varphi \approx 22°$. This result can be checked by calculation. For 20 Hz, the X_c of a 22-nF capacitor is 0.36 MΩ. Together with the 1-MΩ input resistance of the oscilloscope, this means that tan $\varphi = 0.36$ (current through capacitor is 90° ahead of the voltage across it) and arctan 0.36 = 22°. The readout from the screen is thus a fair approximation.

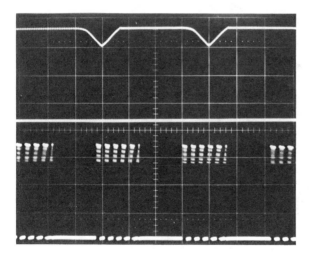

Fig. 5.26 In this double exposure of a pulse generator output, the lower trace indicates vague amplitude, and the upper trace (5 ms/div) indicates 50-Hz dips in output level, pointing to a fault in the pulse-generator power supply.

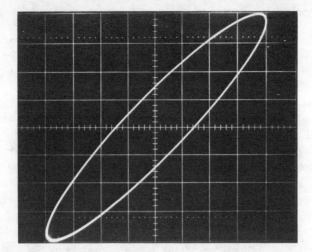

Fig. 5.27 In this *X-Y* display of a 20-Hz sine wave, channel *A* is ac-coupled, *X* deflection, and channel *B* is dc-coupled, *Y* deflection. The fraction cut off the *Y* axis is arcsin φ, with φ being the phase shift between the *X* and *Y* signals.

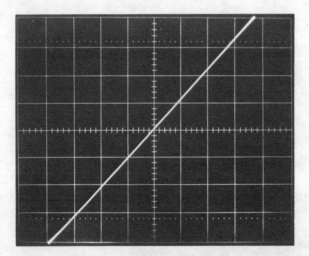

Fig. 5.28 An *X-Y* display of a 1-kHz sine wave, with the same input coupling of the oscilloscope as for the previous illustration.

Already it will be clear that at 1 kHz this effect is no longer noticeable. See Fig. 5.28, where X and Y are in phase with the same oscilloscope input couplings.

5.11 FLOATING MEASUREMENTS ON TV RECEIVERS

Section 2.4 described how common-mode signals can be rejected by operating the oscilloscope in the $A - B$ mode.

THE $A - B$ MODE MUST NEVER BE USED FOR REJECTING THE LINE SUPPLY VOLTAGE.

This application of the $A - B$ mode could be considered when signals have their zero level directly coupled to the line supply voltage. This is found in a great number of TV receivers and is illustrated in Fig. 5.29. The illustration shows a simplified power supply of a typical TV receiver, equipped with both tubes and transistors. Node A of the Graetz diode bridge D is directly connected to the common ($\triangledown$) or chassis. Since the power cord does not usually possess a ground ($\perp$) lead, this has not been included in Fig. 5.29.

But in the oscilloscope the common ($\triangledown$) and the ground ($\perp$) are very often connected together. For this reason the common connection of the oscilloscope cannot be connected to the chassis of the TV receiver. This would mean that the 220-V terminals are connected to ground ($\perp$) via the diodes of bridge D, causing a short circuit. At the very least the fuses VL would be blown, but very often the diodes D have to be replaced as

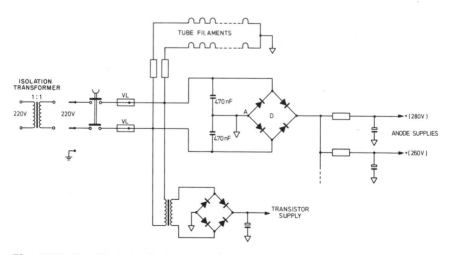

Fig. 5.29 Simplified circuit of a TV receiver power supply.

well. Also, depending on the local 220-V supply, the filaments of half of the tubes may temporarily be connected to double the voltage.

Now, one may initially think that since both oscilloscope inputs have 1-MΩ input impedance, if the $A - B$ mode is used without ground connections, everything will be alright. But if the operator accidently touches both instruments at the same time, a lethal electrical shock may be received. Thus for safety this procedure must never be permitted.

The only solution to this when making measurements on TV receivers is to use an isolation transformer, with separated primary and secondary windings (see Fig. 5.29).

Note This not only applies when connecting an oscilloscope to a TV receiver, but also for other equipment, such as TV pattern generators and digital voltmeters.

By means of the separation transformer, the TV receiver is made to float with respect to ground. Nevertheless, care should always be taken when working on TV receivers.

5.12 EXERCISES

For each exercise, circle the answer you believe is correct.

1. The duty cycle of a periodic single pulse-wave voltage is:

(A) The period time between two successive pulses

(B) The ratio of the pulse-width time and repetition time

(C) The time between the positive and negative slopes of the pulse

2. The rise time of a 10-MHz oscilloscope is:

(A) 3.5 ns

(B) 35 ns

(C) 0.1 μs

3. A 120-MHz oscilloscope with a probe with rise time $T_{pr} = 3.5$ ns is connected to a Schmitt trigger output, for which the transient rise time T_{st} is to be measured. The rise time measured from the screen of the oscilloscope is $T_s = 11$ ns. The actual rise time T_{st} of the Schmitt trigger output voltage is:

(A)   9 ns

(B) 10 ns

(C) 11 ns

4. A 50-Ω coaxial cable connects a pulse generator with a 50-Ω output impedance to an oscilloscope with 1-MΩ input resistance. A 50-Ω termination resistor is required at:

(A) The pulse generator side only

(B) The oscilloscope side only

(C) Both at the pulse generator side and at the oscilloscope side

5. Overcompensation of the probe adjustment for high-frequency sine waves result in a display of which the amplitude is:

(A) Too high

(B) Correct

(C) Too low

6. A dual-trace oscilloscope is operated in the X-Y mode, with X via the Y_A channel. The Y_A channel input is dc-coupled; the Y_B channel input is ac-coupled.
This setting causes a substantial measuring error for sine waves:

(A) Below 40 Hz

(B) Around 1 kHz

(C) Above 100 kHz

MEASURING EXAMPLES

The first part of the chapter details basic experiments to demonstrate the influence of the oscilloscope upon the device under test. In the succeeding paragraphs the capabilities of special oscilloscope features are illustrated by practical applications. Where test and measuring instruments are required for the experiments, the type numbers of suitable instruments from the Philips range are shown in parentheses in the illustrations.

6.1 BASIC EXPERIMENTS

Loading Effect in DC Measurements

Oscilloscopes can measure voltages ranging from microvolts to kilovolts (the latter with the aid of probes). The overall accuracy is on the order of 2 to 5%. As explained in Sec. 4.2, this accuracy may be less if the source impedance R_s is not very small with respect to the oscilloscope input impedance ($R_{in} = 1\ M\Omega$) (see Fig. 4.1).

The fraction of the voltage V_s appearing at the oscilloscope input is:

$$V_{osc} = \frac{R_{in}}{R_{in} + R_s} \cdot V_s$$

This effect is demonstrated in the following exercise.

Measuring Procedure

Equipment Required:

- 1 DC power supply (> 10 V)
- 1 Oscilloscope
- 1 Passive 10 : 1 probe
- 1 Resistor, 1 MΩ
- 1 Resistor, 100 kΩ
- 1 Potentiometer, 1 kΩ
- 2 Single-pole switches
- Coaxial measuring cables

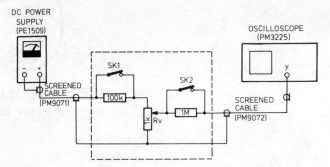

Fig. 6.1 Measuring arrangement using an oscilloscope in a high-ohmic circuit.

Initial Setup

SET THE POWER SUPPLY TO:	SET THE OSCILLOSCOPE TO:

10-V maximum current

AMPL/DIV: 2 V
Input coupling: DC
TIME/DIV: 0.1 ms
TRIG source: INT
TRIG slope: + or −
TRIG mode: NORMAL
TRIG level: TOP

The Philips oscilloscope PM 3225 will show a trace without signal as the AUTO free run circuit is always operative. Other oscilloscopes should be switched to the AUTO mode.

First, switch the vertical input channel to the 0-V position and rotate the Y POSITION control knob until the horizontal trace coincides with the lowest graticule line. This is now the 0-V reference level on the screen.

Next, switch the oscilloscope to the dc-coupled input mode and read the voltage from the screen for the various settings of R_v with $Sk1$ and $Sk2$ closed. The input resistance of the PM 3225 is $R_{in} = 1$ MΩ.

Question 1: What will be the result on the screen if only Sk2 is opened? Check this.

Question 2: What will be the result on the screen if only Sk1 is opened? Set the AMPL/DIV switch to 20 mV/div and check the result.

Question 3: What will be the result on the screen if both Sk2 and Sk1 are opened? Check the results.

Question 4: As seen from the oscilloscope side, which resistor represents R_s in the formula?

Note: To avoid hum on the dc signal, coaxial cables are preferred to plastic-insulated measuring leads.

Replace the coaxial cable between the oscilloscope and the measuring point by a passive 10:1 probe, as shown in Fig. 6.2. The input resistance of a 10:1 passive probe is 10 MΩ (in combination with the oscilloscope). Start with the AMPL/DIV switch set to 0.2 V and repeat the procedure. Check the results on the screen by calculation.

Loading Effect in AC Measurements

Stray capacitances are noticeable with alternating voltages. The oscilloscope in Fig. 6.1 has an input impedance of 1 MΩ ‖ 25 pF. Thus, at 1 MHz the X_c of the 25-pF stray capacitance is

$$X_c = \frac{1}{2\pi \times 10^6 \times 25 \times 10^{-12}}$$

$$= 6.37 \text{ k}\Omega$$

The result is a much heavier load for the measuring point due to the 25-pF stray capacitance than to the 1-MΩ input resistance (at 1 MHz still). The measuring cable from the oscilloscope to the device under text has considerable influence also. One meter of coaxial cable possesses about 100-pF stray capacitance. As discussed in Sec. 4.2, the use of a 10:1 passive probe improves the measuring results.

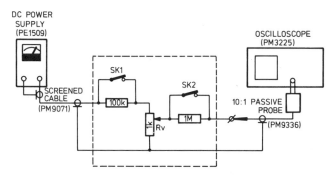

Fig. 6.2 Using the 10:1 passive probe while measuring in a high-ohmic circuit.

Measuring Procedure

Equipment Required:

- 1 Sine-wave generator, 100 kHz
- 1 Oscilloscope
- 1 Passive 10 : 1 probe
- 1 Resistor, 600 Ω
- 1 Resistor, 12 kΩ
- 1 Single-pole switch
- Coaxial measuring cables

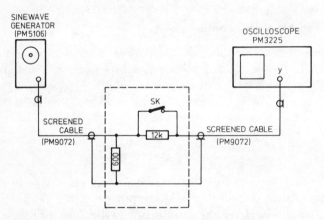

Fig. 6.3 Taking ac measurements in a high-ohmic circuit.

Initial Setup

SET THE SINE-WAVE GENERATOR TO:	SET THE OSCILLOSCOPE TO:
FREQ: 1 kHz	AMPL/DIV: 2 V
AMPL: halfway maximum	Input coupling: DC
	TIME/DIV: 0.5 ms
	TRIG source: INT
	TRIG slope: +
	TRIG mode: NORMAL
	TRIG level: TOP

As shown in Fig. 6.3, the 600-Ω resistor terminates the sine-wave generator, which has an output impedance of 600 Ω too. With switch Sk closed, adjust the AMPL control of the generator until the amplitude on the screen is 6 divisions peak-to-peak. Increase the frequency to 100 kHz; if necessary, readjust the amplitude to 6 divisions. Set the TIME/DIV switch to 50 μs. Now open switch Sk and observe the result. Read and notice the new peak-to-peak amplitude.

If the peak-to-peak amplitude reads $0.7 \times 6 = 4.2$ divisions, this means that the X_c of the coaxial cable in parallel with the 25 pF of the oscilloscope input is also 12 kΩ. From this, it follows that $X_{total} = 132$ pF; thus, the cable capacitance is $C_c = 132 - 25 = 107$ pF.

Question: If X_{total} is indeed 12 kΩ, why is the amplitude on the screen not $0.5 \times 6 = 3$ divisions?

Note: Two separate plastic-insulated measuring leads will have less stray capacitance, depending on the length of the leads. Nevertheless, coaxial cable is preferred at higher frequencies, because the stray capacitances remain constant. This makes it easier for calculation to eliminate the effect of stray capacitances in the measuring results. Moreover, the pickup of hum and other unwanted signals is rejected.

Replace the coaxial cable between the oscilloscope and the measuring point by a passive 10:1 probe. See Fig. 6.4.

Set the AMPL/DIV switch on the oscilloscope to 0.2 V. Repeat the procedure and notice the difference at 100 kHz. The advantage of using a 10:1 passive probe at higher frequencies becomes evident from the difference demonstrated.

Note: Before operation, adjust the probe according to Fig. 4.8.

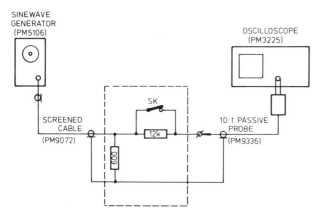

Fig. 6.4 Using the 10:1 passive probe while measuring in a high-ohmic circuit.

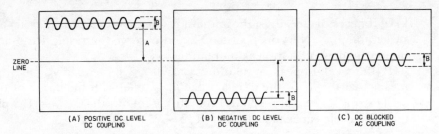

Fig. 6.5 Measuring small ac voltages superimposed on a dc voltage by means of ac/dc coupling of the oscilloscope.

Measurements with AC- and DC-Coupled Inputs

Sometimes an ac voltage to be displayed may be superimposed on a dc level, for example, ripple in a power supply unit. To measure such a voltage, use is made of the ac/dc input coupling switch. In the ac-coupled mode, a series capacitor is internally switched between the input terminal and the attenuator stage of the oscilloscope. The dc component in the signal is thus blocked in this mode. This effect is demonstrated in Fig. 6.5. However, at lower frequencies, ac coupling causes attenuation (Sec. 2.1) and phase shift (Sec. 5.10). These effects are demonstrated in this exercise.

Measuring Procedure

Equipment Required:

- 1 Function generator
- 1 Oscilloscope
- 1 Resistor, 600 Ω
- 1 Passive 10:1 probe
- 1 Adapter, BNC male–banana female
- Coaxial measuring cables

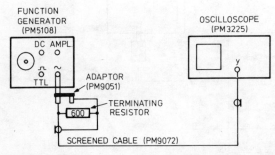

Fig. 6.6 Measuring setup for demonstrating the effects of ac/dc coupling of the oscilloscope.

Initial Setup

SET THE FUNCTION
GENERATOR TO:

FREQ: 1 kHz
AMPL: 4 V peak-to-peak
DC-OFFSET: 0 V
WAVEFORM: SINEWAVE

SET THE OSCILLOSCOPE TO:

AMPL/DIV: 2 V
Input coupling: DC
TIME/DIV: 0.5 ms
TRIG source: INT
TRIG slope: +
TRIG mode: NORMAL
TRIG level: TOP

The 600-Ω resistor terminates the function generator, which has a 600-Ω output resistor too. A sine wave of 2 divisions is displayed. Adjust the Y POSITION control of oscilloscope so that the sine wave is at the center of the screen.

Add +5 V (or −5 V) to the signal and observe the result on the screen. An adjustable dc offset from −5 to +5 V can be added in the Philips function generator, PM 5108. If this instrument is not available, a power supply or dry battery may be connected in series with the signal.

Next attenuate the sine wave 10 times (−20 dB), maintaining the 5-V dc offset. Switch the INPUT COUPLING to AC and AMPL/DIV switch to 0.2 V. The attenuated sine wave is displayed at the center of the screen again with 2 divisions amplitude. Now switch the INPUT COUPLING back to DC.

Question: Explain the result on the screen.

Modify the test setup to that shown in Fig. 6.7.

CHANGE OSCILLOSCOPE
SETTINGS:

AMPL/DIV: 1 V
Input coupling: AC
TIME/DIV: 100 ms
TRIG source: EXT

CHANGE FUNCTION GENERATOR
SETTINGS:

FREQ: 2 kHz
AMPL: 6 V peak-to-peak
DC OFFSET: 0 V

A vertical line of 6 divisions moves over the screen. Move this line symmetrically around the center of the screen by means of the Y POSITION control. Switch the function generator frequency to 2 Hz and observe the amplitude of the sine wave. (In Fig. 6.7 the −3 dB point of the vertical amplifier in the ac-coupled mode is 2 Hz.)

Question: Explain the new amplitude of the 2-Hz sinewave.

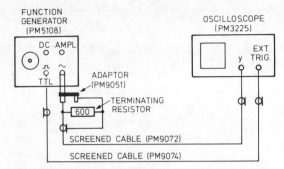

Fig. 6.7 Measuring setup for demonstrating the effects of ac/dc coupling of the oscilloscope.

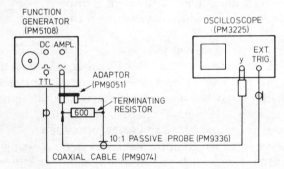

Fig. 6.8 Measuring setup for demonstrating the effects of ac/dc coupling of the oscilloscope, while utilizing a 10:1 passive probe.

Next, with these new settings, operate the ac/dc input coupling switch and observe:

1. The difference in amplitudes

2. The difference in horizontal place of the crossing points of the sine wave with the center axis on the screen

Question: Calculate the value and check the result on the screen.

Set the function generator frequency to 20 Hz and the OUTPUT WAVE-FORM control to SQUAREWAVE. Set the oscilloscope TIME/DIV switch to 20 ms. Again operate the ac/dc input coupling switch and observe the difference. Compare the result with Fig. 2.1.

Keep the input coupling in the ac mode, but replace the cable to the *Y* input by a 10:1 passive probe and set the AMPL/DIV to 0.1 V.

Note: Before operation, adjust the probe according to Fig. 4.8.

Compare the result with the ac-coupled mode of the previous exercise. The difference is explained with the aid of Fig. 6.9.

Capacitor C in Fig. 6.9 denotes that the oscilloscope is ac-coupled. The high-frequency compensation capacitors of the probe and the stray capacitances of the oscilloscope input are neglected at these low frequencies (20 Hz).

Without a probe, R_{probe} can be thought of as 0 Ω. So far as the terminated function generator is concerned, the input RC time of the oscilloscope is given by $R_{\text{in}} \times C$. Together *with* the probe, this RC time becomes

$$(R_{\text{probe}} + R_{\text{in}}) \times C = 10 \times R_{\text{in}} \times C$$

Consequently, the setup illustrated in Fig. 6.8 will provide better results than that in Fig. 6.7. The photograph in Fig. 6.10 is taken from a dual-trace oscilloscope, the upper trace without the use of a probe, the lower

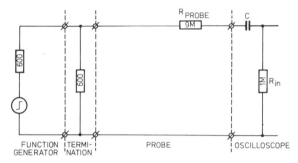

Fig. 6.9 Equivalent circuit diagram of Fig. 6.8.

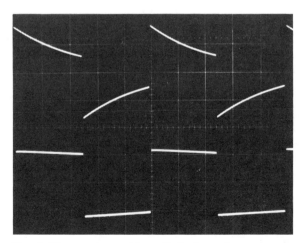

Fig. 6.10 TIME/DIV = 10 ms. Both channels are ac-coupled at the input, with the upper trace directly coupled and the lower trace coupled via a 10:1 passive probe. Note that the lower trace still shows some droop (see Fig. 5.3).

one with a probe. Note that the lower pulse also shows some droop, but this is 10 times less than in the upper trace.

Accurate Phase Measurements (Dual Trace)

Phase shifts are practically always experienced in connection with sinusoidal waveforms. Basically, with any periodic waveform one could define 1 period time as 360° and speak about phase shift instead of time delay between two signals.

In this exercise the time delay between two sine waves is observed, and from this the phase shift is calculated. One period time represents 360°, and any fraction of the period time means a part of 360°. If, for example, 1 sine wave occupies 9 divisions on the screen, then each division represents 40°.

Measuring Procedure

Equipment required:

• 1 Sine-wave generator, 100 kHz
• 1 Dual-trace oscilloscope
• 1 Resistor, 1 kΩ
• 1 Polyester capacitor, 10 nF
• Coaxial measuring cables

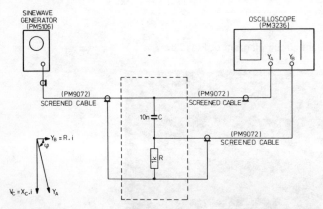

Fig. 6.11 Measurement setup demonstrating phase measurements.

Initial Setup

SET THE SINE-WAVE
GENERATOR TO:

AMPL: 6 V peak-to-peak
FREQ: 1 kHz

SET THE OSCILLOSCOPE TO:

AMPL/DIV Y_A: 1 V

AMPL/DIV Y_B: 50 mV

Input coupling

Y_A and Y_B: AC

CHOP/ALT: CHOP

TRIG source: Y_B

TRIG slope: +

TRIG mode: NORMAL

TRIG level: adjusted to 0 V

TIME/DIV: 0.1 ms calibrated

Note: First adjust both traces exactly to midscale with the Y POSITION controls. Channel Y_A measures the voltage across the entire RC combination; the voltage at channel Y_B is in phase with the current through R and C. At 1 kHz X_c is:

$$X_c = \frac{1}{2\pi fC} \approx 16 \text{ k}\Omega$$

Together with the 1-kΩ resistor this leads to a phase shift φ given by

$$\tan \varphi = X_c/R = 16$$

from which $\varphi = 86°$ (see Fig. 6.11)

The result at 1 kHz is as shown in Fig. 6.12. From the photograph it can be seen that the phase shift is about 2.4 divisions. A whole period, or 360°, lasts 10 divisions; thus the phase shift φ is 86°, as anticipated.

Next, the FREQUENCY control is set to 100 kHz, and the AMPL/DIV controls of channels Y_B and Y_A are set to 1 V.

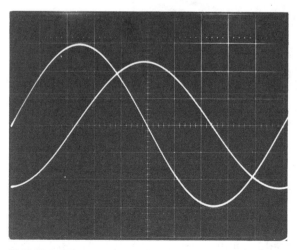

Fig. 6.12 The TIME/DIV switch is set to 0.1 ms/div. One period is 10 divisions.

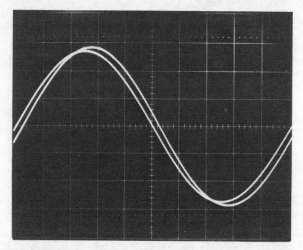

Fig. 6.13 The TIME/DIV switch is set to 1 μs/div. Direct reading of the phase shift becomes inaccurate.

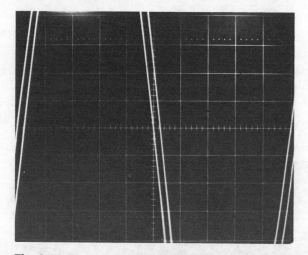

Fig. 6.14 The TIME/DIV switch is set as in Fig. 6.13, but the AMPL/DIV setting is increased.

At 100 kHz X_c = 160 Ω and with R = 1 kΩ, tan φ is

$$\tan \varphi = \frac{160}{1000} = 0.16$$

$$\varphi = 9.1°$$

This is difficult to read from the screen in a straightforward manner. Refer to Fig. 6.13; the TIME/DIV switch is set to 1 μs/div. Now increase the AMPL/DIV control of both channels to 0.2 V/div. The result may be as illustrated in Fig. 6.14. As a next step, increase the TIME/DIV setting to 0.5 μs/div and operate the x5 MAGN switch (valid for the PM3226 in Fig. 6.11). After some readjustment of the TRIGGER LEVEL and X POSITION controls, the result should be as shown in Fig. 6.15. From Fig. 6.13 it is known that 1 period lasts 10 μs (100 kHz), while the time delay as read from Fig. 6.15 is 2.5 × 0.1 = 0.25 μs. From this the phase shift φ follows from

$$\varphi = \frac{0.25}{10} \times 360° = 9°$$

Note 1 As previously mentioned, with these measurements it is extremely important that both traces are *exactly* adjusted at the horizontal center axis of the screen before applying signals. This should be checked each time that one of the AMPL/DIV settings is changed.

· *Note 2* It will be clear that these results at 100 kHz cannot be obtained with an *X-Y* measurement. This is explained in Chap. 7, relating to specification point 6.9 of the PM 3240, which was used to make the photograph.

Pulse and Rise-Time Measurements in the ns Area

Section 5.2 gives the pulse definitions, and Sec. 5.4 explains how rise times are calculated. This exercise demonstrates how measurements are affected by the limitations of the oscilloscope or by probe loading effects.

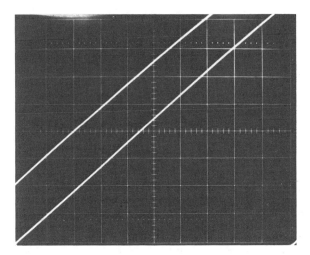

Fig. 6.15 The AMPL/DIV setting is the same as in Fig. 6.14, but the TIME/DIV setting is increased to 0.1 μs/div (0.5 μs/div plus x5 MAGN).

Measuring Procedure

Equipment Required:

- 1 Oscilloscope without delay line (optional)
- 1 Oscilloscope with delay line
- 1 Pulse generator, variable rise time, 6 ns $\leq T_r \leq$ 500 ms
- 1 Pulse generator, $T_r = 1$ ns (optional)
- 1 Resistor, 1 kΩ
- 1 Capacitor, 12 pF
- 1 50Ω termination resistor
- 1 10:1 passive probe, $T_r \leq 2$ ns
- 1 BNC T-piece, 1 × male, 2 × female
- 1 BNC coupling piece, 2 × female
- 1 Adaptor, BNC male–banana female
- 2 Coaxial measuring cables, 50 Ω

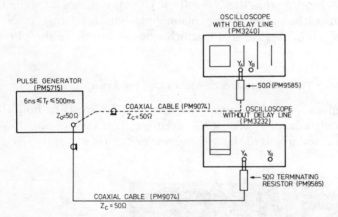

Fig. 6.16 Measuring setup for pulse measurements.

Initial Setup

SET THE PULSE GENERATOR TO:

Pulse repetition: 1 μs
Delay: minimum
Pulse duration: 100 ns range
Rise time T_r: minimum
Fall time T_f: minimum
Output voltage: 1.5 V

SET BOTH OSCILLOSCOPES TO:

Channel Y_A only
AMPL/DIV: 0.1 V
Input coupling: DC
TIME/DIV: 0.2 μs
x5 MAGN: on
TRIG source: Y_A
TRIG slope: +
TRIG coupling: DC
TRIG mode: AUTO
TRIG level: adjusted

First, connect the oscilloscope without a delay line (PM 3232) to the pulse generator, as indicated in Fig. 6.16 (note the 50-Ω termination). The waveform obtained is as shown in Fig. 6.17; the pulse duration is adjusted to about 300 ns. As explained in Sec. 2.5, the positive slope cannot be observed from the screen. Next, connect the oscilloscope with a delay line (PM 3240) to the pulse generator; a waveform as shown in Fig. 6.18 should be obtained.

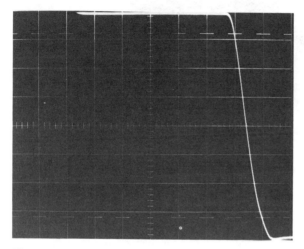

Fig. 6.17 Display of an impulse on a 10-MHz oscilloscope without delay line (PM 3232). The leading edge is missing. Time-base speed is 40 ns/div (0.2 μs/div + x5 MAGN).

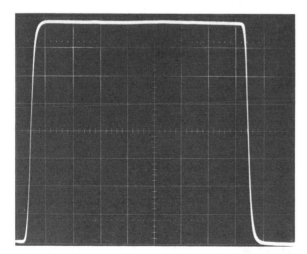

Fig. 6.18 Same pulse as shown in Fig. 6.17 but displayed on a 50-MHz oscilloscope with delay line (PM 3240). Time-base speed is also 40 ns/div.

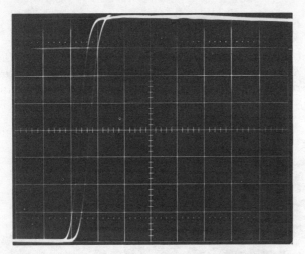

Fig. 6.19 Response of a 50-MHz oscilloscope (PM 3240) to a pulse of 1-ns rise time. The fastest response of the oscilloscope is displayed at 10-ns/div time-base speed. Delayed pulse from probe (T_r = 1.2 ns) with longer cable.

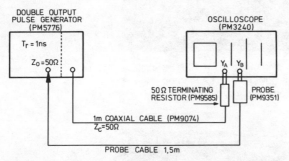

Fig. 6.20 Measuring the oscilloscope's response to pulses with relatively very short rise times.

Comparison of the two pictures shows:

1. Rough estimation of the relative time delay in the horizontal circuits of the PM 3232, with respect to the PM 3240.

2. The fall times of the pulses are different. This is caused by the bandwidth of the PM 3232 oscilloscope, which is 10 MHz (T_r = 35 ns), and the bandwidth of the PM 3240, which is 50 MHz (T_r = 7 ns).

Section 5.4 explained that the rise time of an oscilloscope must be measured with a pulse whose rise time $T_{\text{pulse}} \ll T_{\text{scope}}$, as demonstrated in Fig. 6.19. The measuring arrangement is shown in Fig. 6.20.

Two pulses appear simultaneously at two outputs of a pulse generator (PM 5776). As can be seen in Fig. 6.19, two pulses appear, both with T_r slightly less than 7 ns. Thus from the photograph, it can be understood that the oscilloscope's response is within specification, in accordance with the details given in Sec. 5.4.

As the probe cable is longer than the terminated coax cable, the probe pulse appears later. Theoretically, T_{probe} should be considered also, but for the probe used (PM 9351) T_{probe} is specified as 1.2 ns. This would lead to

$$T_{screen}^2 = T_{pulse}^2 + T_{probe}^2 + T_{scope}^2$$
$$= \quad 1 \quad + \quad 1.4 \quad + \quad 49 \quad = 51.4$$

$$T_{screen} = 7.17 \text{ ns}$$

Without the probe, $T_{screen} = \sqrt{49 + 1} = 7.07$ ns, which means in practice that the influence of the probe on the measured rise can be disregarded.

The influence of T_{pulse} is demonstrated in Fig. 6.21, employing the pulse generator used in Fig. 6.16. Now it follows that

$$T_{screen}^2 = T_{pulse}^2 + T_{probe}^2 + T_{scope}^2$$
$$= \quad 36 \quad + \quad 1.4 \quad + \quad 49 \quad = 86.4$$

$$T_{screen} = 9.30 \text{ ns}$$

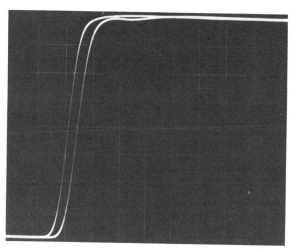

Fig. 6.21 Same as Fig. 6.19, but now the rise time of the pulse generator is 6 ns. Transient time on the screen becomes longer.

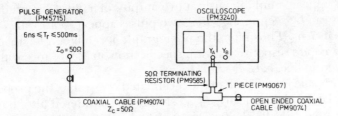

Fig. 6.22 Measuring cable reflections.

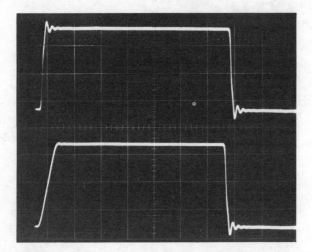

Fig. 6.23 Pulses with longer rise times contain less higher harmonics and give less rise to reflections (lower trace rise time). Time-base speed is 50 ns/div.

which is in accordance with the result (second pulse in Fig. 6.21) as far as it can be read from the screen.

Figure 5.8 demonstrates that wrong termination of a transmission line results in reflections. The connection arrangement shown in Fig. 6.22 also leads to reflections, as can be seen from the upper trace in Fig. 6.23.

For the upper trace, the rise time T_r and the fall time T_f were set at 6 ns (minimum) at the pulse generator. However, the extent the signal is distorted depends upon the frequency content of the pulse wave, as demonstrated in the lower trace of Fig. 6.23. The rise time is varied at the pulse generator until the disturbance disappears. For the purpose of demonstration the fall time is kept the same (time-base speed of 50 ns/div).

By the Fourier analysis described in Sec. 5.3, for the ideal pulse it can be proved that the content of the higher harmonics is much less in a trapezium waveform than in an "ideal" square wave. Thus the longer the rise and fall times, the less frequency content and the less the distortion.

Cutting off higher frequencies can also be accomplished by a low-pass *RC* filter. This can be demonstrated with the circuit arrangement shown in Fig. 6.24.

Figure 6.25 shows the results in a double-exposed photograph. The steeper transient is measured at point *A* in Fig. 6.24. Care must be taken with grounding the probe tip, to avoid ringing (see also Fig. 4.7). The other slope is the well-known "*RC* curve" for charging a capacitor *C* via a resistor *R*. This curve is very smooth without any ringing.

Note Behind this measurement a pitfall is hidden. The 1-kΩ resistor forms a relatively high-ohmic source impedance. Moreover, the input capacitance of the probe tip (11 pF of the PM 9351) is not small compared to the 12 pF used in Fig. 6.24 and is connected in parallel with it during the measurement. To a great extent, this influences the result on the screen.

It is known, and can be mathematically proved, that the 10 to 90% rise time T_{RC} of an "*RC* curve" is given by

$$T_{RC} = 2.2\ RC$$

Now the actual rise time at point B can be calculated from the result on the screen. From Fig. 6.25 the rise time T_{screen} can be measured as

$$T_{\text{screen}} = 2.5 \text{ divisions} \times 20 \text{ ns/div} = 50 \text{ ns}$$

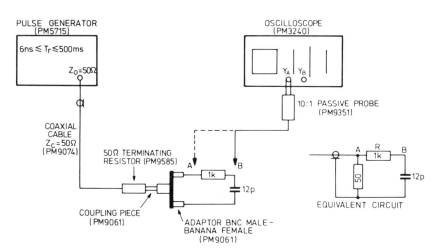

Fig. 6.24 Measuring pulse response of a *RC* network.

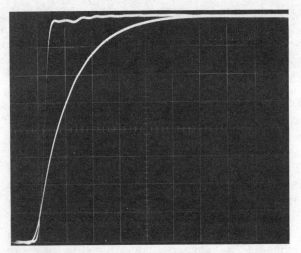

Fig. 6.25 Higher frequencies of the impulse are cut off by low-pass *RC* filter, resulting in smoother pulses. Time-base speed is 20 ns/div.

From this it follows total RC_t time

$$RC_t = \frac{50}{2.2} = 22.7 \text{ ns}$$

Knowing that the source impedance is 1 kΩ, this means that

$$C_t = \frac{22.7}{1000} \text{ nF}$$

$$= 22.7 \text{ pF}$$

Of this value, 11 pF is the capacitance of the probe tip, leaving 11.7 pF for capacitor *C* (Fig. 6.24), which is very close. However, this could also be an unknown stray capacitance.

The actual rise time at point B is thus

$$T_B = 2.2 \times 1 \times 11.7 = 25.7 \text{ ns}$$

Therefore, the measured rise time at point B is 50 ns on the screen, but the actual rise time is about 26 ns. This kind of effect should be remembered when measuring from high-ohmic sources. But if the source impedance and the probe capacitance are known, the right answer can be calculated as shown. For this reason the value of the probe capacitance is printed on the probe casing. It will be clear that the smaller the probe capacitance, the less the influence on the actual rise time and the better the measuring result. When the influence on the rise time is an important factor, FET probes could be used, possessing only 2 to 3 pF at the tip.

Further measuring examples may be found in the booklet "Digital Exercises," published in the present series of Philips booklets.

Time-Domain Reflectometry (TDR)

If a transmission line is not terminated at the far end by its characteristic impedance, reflections occur (see Sec. 5.5). This phenomenon can also be used to determine faults in transmission lines. Although special TDR oscilloscopes are on the market, the basic setup is given in this section. The results on the screen are explained.

Measuring Procedure

Equipment Required:

- 1 Pulse generator
- 1 Coaxial cable $\geq$ 10 m, $Z_c = 50\ \Omega$
- 1 Oscilloscope with delay line
- 1 Passive 10:1 probe
- 1 50-Ω termination resistor
- 1 Adaptor, banana female–BNC male
- 1 T-piece BNC
- Coaxial measuring cables

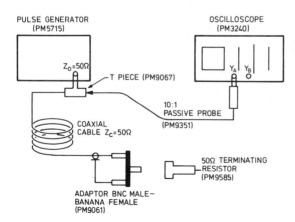

Fig. 6.26 Demonstration setup for TDR measurements.

Initial Setup

SET PULSE GENERATOR TO:

AMPL: 5 V
Pulse rep. time: 10 μs
Mode: square wave
DC offset: zero (PM5715)
Delay time: minimum

SET OSCILLOSCOPE TO:

AMPL/DIV: 0.1 V
Input coupling: DC
CHOP/ALT: Y_A only
TRIG source: Y_A
TRIG slope: +
TRIG mode: AUTO
TRIG level: adjusted
TIME/DIV: 5 μs

With the far end open, the result on the screen is as shown in Fig. 6.27. The final amplitude is reached in two steps. At the moment the pulse generator meets the 50 Ω of the cable itself, the output is at nominal value (see midscale dots). A reflection takes place at the open end. When this reflection feeds back to the pulse generator output, it "tells" the generator that the far end is open, and the open emf voltage of the pulse generator appears (see Sec. 5.5 also).

Now, if the TIME/DIV switch is set to 0.1 μs, the trace shown in Fig. 6.28 will be displayed on the screen. The midscale dots in Fig. 6.27 are extended now to about 3 divisions.

From the screen it can be derived that one reflection takes about 0.34 μs, or 340 ns. The velocity of a signal in a coaxial cable is about 0.7c, where c is the velocity of light ($c = 3 \times 10^8$ m/s). Assuming a cable

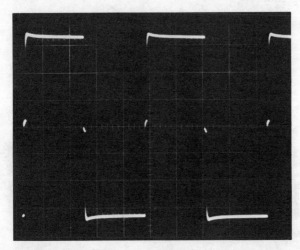

Fig. 6.27 The open emf voltage at the beginning of the cable is reached after the second step. Midscale dots indicate reflections. TIME/DIV = 5 μs.

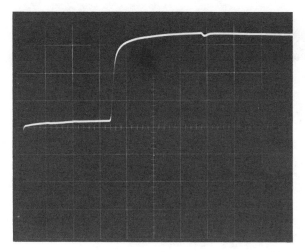

Fig. 6.28 The time scale in Fig. 6.27 enlarged. Reflection time can be measured now. TIME/DIV = 0.1 μs.

length of L_m, it will take $2L/0.7c$ seconds before the signal returns as a reflection to the pulse generator output. Thus in the case of Fig. 6.28 the cable length is calculated as

$$\frac{2L}{0.7 \times 3 \times 10^8} = 340 \times 10^{-9}$$

$$L = 35.7 \text{ m}$$

However, the accuracy of this result is determined by the time-base accuracy, 2 to 3%, which is ± 1 m here.

Short-circuiting the far end results in the waveform shown in Fig. 6.29. After 340 ns the pulse generator "knows" that its output is short-circuited and the voltage drops to zero. The cable load influences this "ideal" behavior, and zero means "almost" zero, which can be noticed from the offset level with respect to the start.

Terminating the far end with 50 Ω results in the waveform shown in Fig. 6.30. The point of the connection can still be noticed from the screen. At the point of connection at the far end, the impedance does not exactly match the actual characteristic impedance (nonideal cable and nonideal 50-Ω resistor).

Accurate Measurements on FM Signals

The frequency deviation on frequency-modulated (fm) signals can be determined in an accurate way with the aid of the oscilloscope's delayed time base (DTB). However, even without a DTB the frequency deviation can be read from the screen.

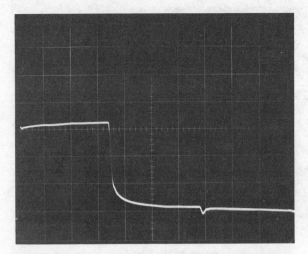

Fig. 6.29 Far end short-circuited; after the reflection the voltage at the generator side drops to almost zero.

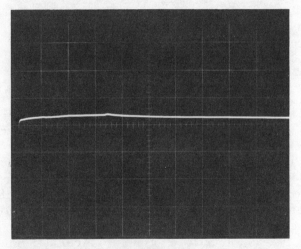

Fig. 6.30 Far end terminated by 50 Ω, close to the characteristic impedance of the cable.

Measuring Procedure

Equipment Required:

• 1 FM generator
• 1 Oscilloscope
• 1 Adaptor, BNC male–banana female
• 1 Termination resistor, 75 Ω
• Connection cable

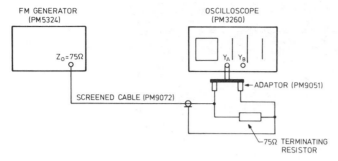

Fig. 6.31 Demonstration setup for frequency-modulated (fm) measurements.

Initial Setup

SET THE FM GENERATOR
PM 5324 TO:

FREQ: 0.5 MHz
Mode: WOB
HF AMPL: Max.; $\geq$ 50 mV

SET THE OSCILLOSCOPE TO:

Channel Y_A only
AMPL/DIV: 10 mV
Input coupling: DC
TIME/DIV: 2 μs
TRIG source: Y_A
TRIG slope: +
TRIG coupling: DC
TRIG mode: AUTO
TRIG level: adjusted

The fm generator *wobbulation* mode is used in order to exaggerate the result on the screen. An explanation is given in Fig. 6.32 where three cycles of the output waveform are shown. The carrier waveform f_c varies according to $f_c \pm \Delta f$, which, when displayed on an oscilloscope, means a variation from $f_c + 3 \Delta f$ to $f_c - 3 \Delta f$ after the third period. When this Δf is high enough, the result may be read directly from the screen (see Fig. 6.33).

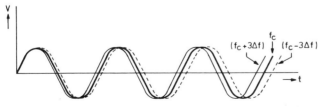

Fig. 6.32 Variation in the zero crossings of fm signal when displayed on an oscilloscope.

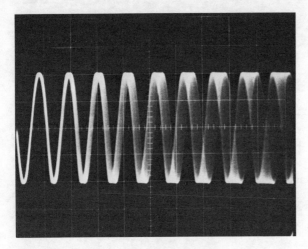

Fig. 6.33 FM signal. TIME/DIV is 2 μs.

From the down-going slope of the 7th cycle, it can be observed that the zero crossing varies from 7.6 to 8.2 divisions. This means a maximum period time of

$$T_{max} = \frac{8.2 \times 2 \times 10^{-6}}{7} = 2.34 \ \mu s$$

or minimum frequency ($f - \Delta f$) of

$$f - \Delta f = \frac{1}{T_{max}} = 0.427 \ \text{MHz}$$

Analog is

$$f + \Delta f = \frac{7}{7.6 \times 2 \times 10^{-6}} = 0.461 \ \text{MHz}$$

$$2 \ \Delta f = 34 \ \text{kHz}$$

giving $2 \ \Delta f = 34$ kHz

If the maximum frequency deviation of $2 \ \Delta f$ is much less, successful use can be made of a delayed time base (DTB). Figure 6.34 shows about 10 periods of the same frequency, but with the 10th positive slope *intensified* by the DTB. Switching over to the DTB mode provides the result shown in Fig. 6.35. The TIME/DIV setting here is 0.1 μs, and the 10th deviation $2 \ \Delta f$ is measured as 2 divisions = 0.2 μs. Thus, *per period* $2 \ \Delta f = 0.02$ μs. Knowing that $f_c = 500$ kHz (1 period is 2 μs),

$$2 \ \Delta f = \frac{0.02}{2} \times 500$$

$$= 5 \ \text{kHz}$$

Note f_c can be measured in the unmodulated mode by counting from 10 to 20 periods on the screen in the appropriate MTB TIME/DIV setting. The deviation in the fm mode is at a maximum on the right-hand side of the screen and here the "time loop" of the DTB should be used.

Accurate Time Measurements with Composite Triggering

Composite triggering allows a stable display of two signals which are not frequency-related (see Sec. 2.6). If one of the signals is a system-standard clock, the pulse repetition rate of incoming signals can be determined

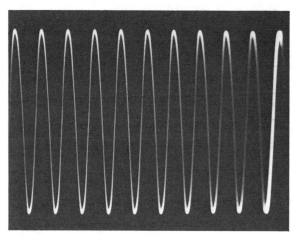

Fig. 6.34 FM signal: TIME/DIV is 2 μs. The positive slope of 10th period is intensified by DTB.

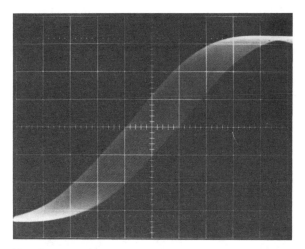

Fig. 6.35 DTB display of Fig. 6.34. TIME/DIV is 0.1 μs. From this, the 2Δf in Fig. 6.34 can be calculated accurately.

rather accurately, as is demonstrated in this example. For the clock signal, use is made in this example of a normal pulse generator, while the pulse repetition rate of another one is determined.

Measuring Procedure

Equipment Required:

- 2 Pulse generators
- 1 Oscilloscope with composite trigger facility
- 2 50-Ω termination resistors
- Coaxial measuring cables

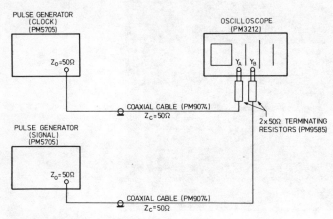

Fig. 6.36 Accurate time measurements utilizing composite triggering.

Initial Setup

SET THE (CLOCK) PULSE
GENERATOR TO:

REP. TIME: $10\ \mu$s
Mode: square wave

SET THE (SIGNAL) PULSE
GENERATOR TO:

REP. TIME: $80–90\ \mu$s
Pulse duration: $2\ \mu$s

SET THE OSCILLOSCOPE TO:

AMPL/DIV Y_A: 2 V
AMPL/DIV Y_B: 2 V
Channel switch: ALT
Input couplings both: DC
TIME/DIV MTB: $10\ \mu$s
TIME/DIV DTB: $0.5\ \mu$s
DTB multiplier: ≈ 8.5
TRIG source: COMP
TRIG slope MTB: +
TRIG couplings both: DC
TRIG mode MTB: AUTO
TRIG mode DTB: START
TRIG level MTB: adjusted

A display similar to that shown in Fig. 6.37 should be obtained. The upper trace shows the clock frequency; the lower trace the incoming signal. Both traces are triggered at the positive slope of the respective signals.

As can be seen from the photograph, it is determined that the signal arrives after the positive slope of the 8th clock pulse, thus after 80 μs. By switching the oscilloscope to the DTB mode, it is possible to measure how long it takes the signal to arrive after the 80 μs. Refer to Fig. 6.38 (the TIME/DIV setting is 0.5 μs); from the photograph it can be seen that

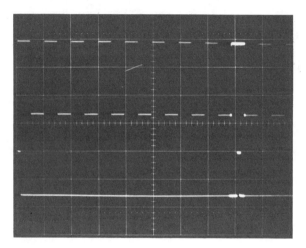

Fig. 6.37 The upper trace is the clock-reference frequency. The lower trace is the signal to be measured.

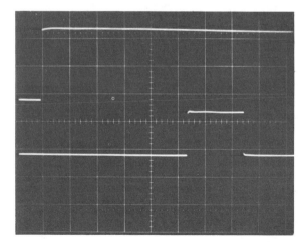

Fig. 6.38 The upper trace shows the positive slope of the 8th clock pulse. The signal arrives with its positive slope after 2.6 μs. TIME/DIV = 0.5 μs.

the delay is 5.2 divisions, meaning $5.2 \times 0.5 = 2.6\ \mu s$. Thus the pulse repetition time of the signal to be tested is $82.6\ \mu s$.

The accuracy of the $2.6\ \mu s$ is known to be as 3% of full scale of the DTB sweep, thus 3% of $5\ \mu s$ ($10 \times 0.5\ \mu s$/div), which is $0.15\ \mu s$. The accuracy of the $80\ \mu s$ is governed by the accuracy of the clock reference, which might be in the order of 10 to 100 parts per million, but this is negligible. Thus the $82.6\ \mu s$ is known with $\pm 0.15\ \mu s$, which means in this case about 0.2%.

Note This result is much below the 3% time-base error, although strongly dependent on the frequency ratio of the two signals. If both the frequencies are about the same, the overall result will not be much below the 3% error. If high accuracies are demanded, a digital frequency counter/timer should be used, if available.

6.2 X-Y MEASUREMENTS

Crossover Distortion in Hi-fi Amplifiers

Although in itself a rather simple measurement, a wrong setting of the oscilloscope may distort the picture, as will be explained while discussing the result.

Measuring Procedure

Equipment Required:

- 1 Low-distortion lf generator
- 1 Audio amplifier (to be tested)
- 1 Oscilloscope
- 2 Passive 1:1 probes
- 1 T-piece BNC

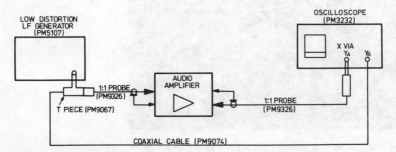

Fig. 6.39 Measuring crossover distortion of an audio amplifier.

Initial Setup

SET THE LF GENERATOR TO:

AMPL: adjusted to amplifier (mV)

FREQ: 1 kHz

Waveform: sine (applicable to PM5107)

Mode: low distortion (PM5107)

SET THE OSCILLOSCOPE TO:

AMPL/DIV Y_A: adjusted to audio ampl.

AMPL/DIV Y_B: 2 mV

Input coupling Y_A and Y_B: AC

TIME/DIV: X via Y_A

In the measuring arrangement shown in Fig. 6.39, a 1:1 passive probe is used to feed the signal from the generator into the amplifier. It might be convenient to clip the probe tip onto the circuitry of the amplifier.

A possible result is shown in Fig. 6.40. Here the sensitivity of the oscilloscope input is extended so much that the picture exceeds the screen. Compare the phase measurement in Sec. 6.1, under Accurate Phase Measurements, although care must be taken in doing so. The "dynamic range" or maximum deflection of an oscilloscope is stated in its specifications. See Sec. 7.2 for the relevant specifications of the PM 3226 (item 2) and the PM 3240 (item 2.6). This specification point may be 24 divisions, which means 3 screen heights of a 8 × 10 cm screen. Outside this range, no harm can occur to the vertical amplifier, but it may be driven into saturation. After having been in saturation, the amplifier needs some time to "recover." The time taken is usually quite short, but it might be visible.

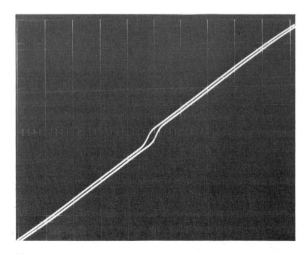

Fig. 6.40 Crossover distortion displayed in *X-Y* mode.

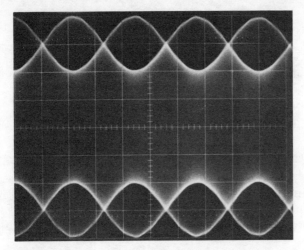

Fig. 6.41 AM signal triggered on carrier.

As soon as the display shown in Fig. 6.40 is obtained, the output stage of the audio amplifier can be adjusted in a dynamic way for minimum distortion.

Modulation Depth of AM Signals

The X-Y mode of an oscilloscope can be usefully employed to determine the modulation depth of amplitude-modulated (am) signals. Basically the same measurement arrangement can be used as shown in Fig. 6.31, but the fm generator is set to the range 0.1 to 0.3 MHz and the modulation mode to am. In the AM-INT mode of the PM 5324 a 1-kHz modulation is applied. The 1-kHz modulating signal is available from a separate terminal on the front panel for trigger purposes. Other frequencies may be used for amplitude modulation in the AM-EXT mode of the generator.

Figures 6.41 through 6.45 show some examples of how an am signal can be displayed. If the modulating signal is not available for trigger purposes (EXT triggering), then displays such as Figs. 6.41 and 6.42 may be obtained. Furthermore, the display in Fig. 6.41 is moving over the screen from left to right, or vice versa. However, from this picture the modulation depth of 0.3 m can be read. Note that the formula of an amplitude-modulated voltage may be written as

$$e = E(1 + m \sin \Omega t) \sin \omega t$$

where
$$E = \text{amplitude of carrier signal}$$
$$m = \text{modulation depth, } 0 \leqslant m \leqslant 1$$
$$\sin \Omega t = \text{modulating signal}$$
$$\sin \omega t = \text{carrier signal}$$

When $m = 0$, only the carrier results, $m = 1$ means 100% modulation depth.

The signal Em sin Ωt is modulating the carrier E sin ωt and varies around its zero level, which in this case is the peak value E of the carrier. Thus, from Fig. 6.41 it follows that E is 3 divisions (peak-to-peak 6 divisions), while $mE = 1$ division. Then by definition $m = \frac{1}{3}$.

If the lf modulating signal is available, then by means of external triggering, the familiar waveform shown in Fig. 6.43 may be obtained.

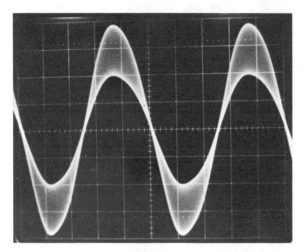

Fig. 6.42 Same as 6.41, but only two periods of carrier are visible. Time-base speed is extended.

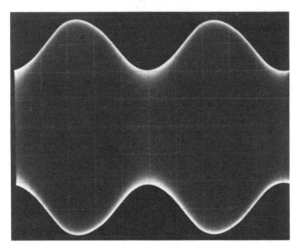

Fig. 6.43 AM signal, triggered externally on modulating signal.

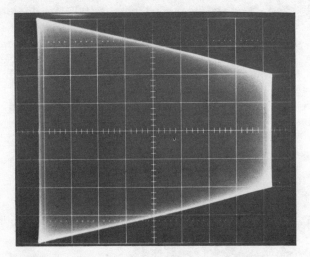

Fig. 6.44 *X-Y* display of am signal, *X*-deflection modulating signal, *Y*-deflection modulated signal.

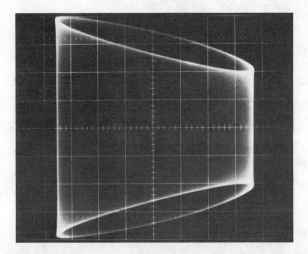

Fig. 6.45 Same as Fig. 6.44, but *X*-deflection input signal is ac-coupled. Due to low frequency of modulating signal (10 Hz), the ellipsoid occurs.

If the lf signal is used for the *X* deflection and the modulated signal for *Y* deflection, then the result will be as shown in Fig. 6.44. If the peak-to-peak value (and not the amplitude) is taken from both the carrier and the modulating signal for the measurement of *m*, then around the vertical center axis it can be seen that the value of the carrier is 6 divisions (peak-to-peak). The variation around this is 2 divisions; thus again $m = \frac{1}{3}$.

As described in Sec. 5.10, ac coupling of the X deflection can lead to distortion in the display. This is shown in Fig. 6.45, where the X-input coupling was ac and the modulating signal 10 Hz, with the same settings as in Fig. 6.44. Apart from a smaller X deflection, an ellipsoid is also visible in the modulation. Thus, this effect is not caused by the modulator circuit in the generator but by a false (ac) input coupling at the oscilloscope input.

Display of the Hysteresis Gap of Schmitt Triggers

The tripping levels are the levels of the input signal at which the output voltage changes its state. The difference in the tripping levels is called the *hysteresis gap*. For integrated Schmitt triggers (for example, the Philips FCL 101), the common-emitter resistance must be connected externally to the IC. If a Schmitt trigger is not available, it may be assembled very easily from discrete components.

Measuring Procedure

Equipment Required:

• 1 lf generator
• 1 Schmitt trigger (to be tested)
• 1 Oscilloscope
• 2 Passive 1 : 1 probes
• 1 Power supply ≥ 10 V
• Measuring cables

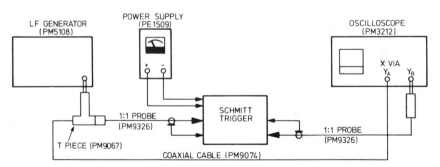

Fig. 6.46 Measuring the tripping levels of a Schmitt trigger.

Initial Setup

SET THE LF GENERATOR TO:

AMPL: 2 V peak-to-peak
FREQ: 1 kHz
Waveform: sine (triangle for PM 5108)

SET THE OSCILLOSCOPE TO:

AMPL/DIV Y_A: 0.1 V
AMPL/DIV Y_B: 1 V
Input coupling: DC
TIME/DIV: X via Y_A

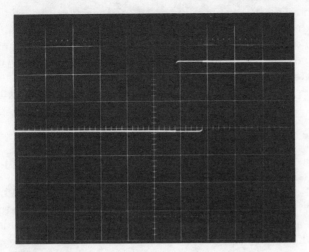

Fig. 6.47 An *X-Y* display of the hysteresis gap of a Schmitt trigger. Left-hand side of screen is adjusted to be 0 V and x-AMPL/DIV is 0.5 V.

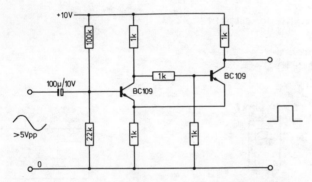

Fig. 6.48 Circuit diagram of the Schmitt trigger tested.

As in Fig. 6.39 two 1 : 1 passive probes are used for connection to the Schmitt trigger. The result is shown in Fig. 6.47.

Before the measurement is started, the 0-V position for the horizontal deflection should be checked and adjusted to coincide with the left hand side of the screen. This is accomplished by setting the AC-0-DC input coupling switch to the "0" position and adjusting the x POSITION control knob. Knowing that the left-hand side is zero volts, and the deflection coefficient is 0.5 V/div, the tripping levels are 2.9 V and 3.4 V, as can be read from the display in Fig. 6.47. The hysteresis gap is thus 3.4 − 2.9 = 0.5 V.

The transients at the output of the Schmitt trigger are too fast to be displayed on the CRT. However, the brightness of the horizontal traces is half at the places where the gap may be observed (Fig. 6.47). If this is not clearly visible, the tripping levels may be determined by measuring the ends of the traces one after the other, from the horizontal center axis, by shifting the picture with the Y POSITION control.

If a Schmitt trigger is not available, a suitable circuit can be constructed, as shown in Fig. 6.48. In fact the display shown in Fig. 6.47 was obtained using this same circuit.

The Oscilloscope Used as Curve tracer

Although the practical value may be limited, it can be useful for educational purposes to display the curves of a transistor. A simple measuring procedure is given here.

Measuring Procedure

Equipment Required:

- 1 Pulse generator with variable rise time
- 1 Function generator
- 1 Oscilloscope
- 4 1:1 passive probes
- 1 Resistor, 10 Ω
- 1 Resistor, 1 kΩ
- 1 Resistor, 100 kΩ
- 1 Coaxial measuring cable
- 1 Transistor to be tested

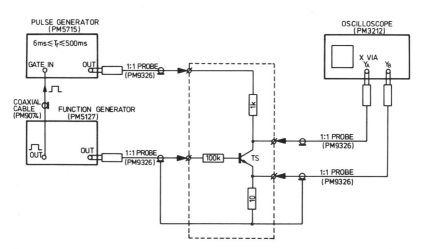

Fig. 6.49 A simple way to visualize the characteristics of a transistor.

Initial Setup

SET THE PULSE GENERATOR TO:
(PM 5715)

SET THE OSCILLOSCOPE TO:

REP. TIME: 10 ms
Duration: 100 μs
T_r and T_f: 50 μs
Mode: EXT

X via Y_A
AMPL/DIV Y_A: 20 mV
AMPL/DIV Y_B: 0.1 V
Input couplings both: DC

SET THE FUNCTION GENERATOR
(PM 5127) TO:

FREQ.: 10 Hz
Mode: triangle
Duty cycle: 0.1–0.3

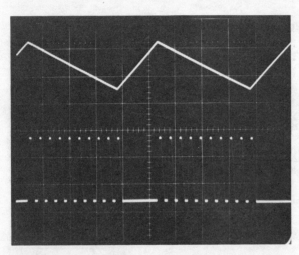

Fig. 6.50 The upper trace is the output of the function generator shown in Fig. 6.49, used to supply the base current. The lower trace shows the collector supply voltage obtained from the pulse generator.

First try to obtain the display illustrated in Fig. 6.50 in order to check the applied voltages with the oscilloscope in the normal Y-t mode. For a good visibility of the transistor curves, the fall times of the pulses should be set to a reasonable value, such that they are clearly visible (see photograph).

At the collector of the transistor under test, V_{CE} can be taken off for X deflection. Across a small emitter resistor (10 Ω), the current I_c through the transistor is visualized ($I_B \approx 0$) as Y deflection. Thus on the screen $I_c = f(V_{CE})$ becomes visible (see Fig. 6.51.).

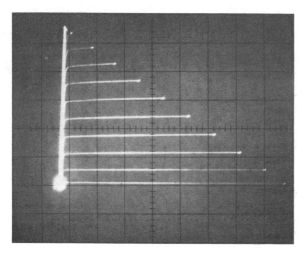

Fig. 6.51 I_c-V_{CE} curves displayed in the X-Y mode.

As can be seen from the lower trace in Fig. 6.50, the collector voltage is usually zero. Hence no current flows through the transistor, and the spot on the screen is at its origin for most of the time. This will result in a very bright spot on the screen. For this reason a storage oscilloscope is used to obtain a picture such as in Fig. 6.51. Moreover, the traces become more visible in this way due to accumulation at the storage mesh (see Sec. 3.1).

X-Y-Y Measurements

If a dual-trace oscilloscope possesses a separate input bus for X deflection, two signals may be displayed simultaneously in the X-Y mode. For this the channel switch selector must be set to the *chopped* mode. A practical example in radio and TV servicing is given here.

Measuring Procedure

Equipment Required:

- 1 TV sweep generator
- 1 Chrominance-luminance TV if unit
- 1 Dual-trace oscilloscope
- Measuring cables

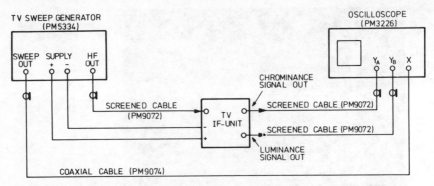

Fig. 6.52 A possible demonstration setup to perform *X-Y-Y* measurements.

Initial Setup

SET THE TV SWEEP GENERATOR
TO:

FREQ.: 30–50 MHz
SWEEP WIDTH: adjusted
CENTER FREQ.: adjusted
+ and − supply: 24 V
Marker: 38.9 MHz

SET THE OSCILLOSCOPE TO:

AMPL/DIV Y_A: 0.1 V
AMPL/DIV Y_B: 0.5 V
Input couplings both: AC
Ext. *X* deflection: operated

The TV if unit is a normal unit supplied by the radio/TV service dealer as a building block of a modern color TV receiver. The TV sweep generator used (Philips PM 5334) also supplies the dc voltage for this if unit. The result should be as illustrated in Fig. 6.53.

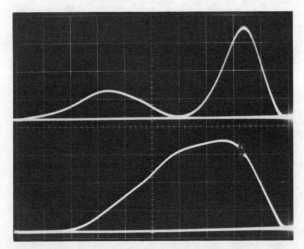

Fig. 6.53 Chrominance and luminance curves (upper and lower, respectively) displayed together in the *X-Y-Y* mode of an oscilloscope.

The upper trace is the chrominance bandpass curve; the lower trace shows the luminance curve. A marker indicates the 38.9 MHz, a characteristic frequency in TV if curves. The marker is also inserted and is frequency adjustable by the TV sweep generator.

6.3 MULTIPLIER APPLICATIONS

Introduction

Section 3.3, under The Multiplier Oscilloscope, described the operation of the multiplying circuit. However, operating a multiplier oscilloscope (Philips PM 3265) may result in unexpected phenomena. The first example shows basic definitions, while in other examples power measurements on semiconductors are performed.

Definition of Positive and Negative Power: *EI* cos φ = 0

From the display on the oscilloscope screen one may observe instants during which the product of the current and voltage (power) is below the zero level or negative, and other instants with a positive power level. With the aid of the measuring setup in Fig. 6.54, the meaning of this is explained further.

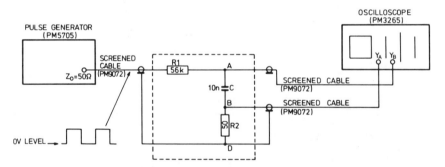

Fig. 6.54 The charging and discharging of a capacitor is used to demonstrate the definition of positive and negative power.

Measuring Procedure

Equipment Required:

- 1 Pulse generator
- 1 Multiplier oscilloscope
- 1 Resistor, 56 kΩ
- 1 Resistor, 50 Ω
- 1 Capacitor, 10 nF
- Coaxial measuring cables

Initial Setup

AMPL: 1 V peak-to-peak
Pulse rep. time: 10 ms
Mode: square wave

AMPL/DIV Y_A: 5 mV
AMPL/DIV Y_B: 500 mV
Input coupling Y_A and Y_B: DC
CHOP/ALT: CHOP
TRIG source: Y_B
TRIG slope: −
TRIG mode: AUTO
TRIG level: adjusted
TIME/DIV: 20 ms

Capacitor C is charged via $R_1 = 56$ kΩ. The voltage across C is measured at point A; the current through it is measured via a small resistor $R_2 = 50$ Ω at point B. The display in Fig. 6.55 shows the current through the capacitor in the upper trace and the voltage across it in the lower trace. The zero level of the latter is the lower level of the pulse. The voltage is thus always either positive or zero.

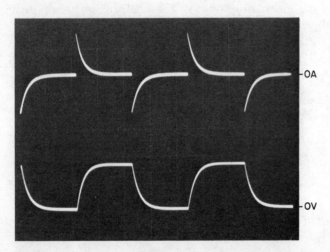

Fig. 6.55 (Upper trace) Current through a capacitor. (Lower trace) voltage across a capacitor.

The upper trace in Fig. 6.55 shows the current peaks. If the voltage goes from zero to positive, the current is positive also. Thus the current through C and R_2 flows from B to D until the capacitor is charged; that is, the upper level is reached in the lower trace. If subsequently the voltage of the pulse generator goes down (to zero volts), the capacitor discharges via R_1 and the source impedance of the generator (50 Ω). During this time the current flows in the opposite direction, from D to B in

R_2. However, during the discharge time, the voltage across the capacitor is positive, although it is decreasing. This means that the product of voltage and current (power) will be negative during discharge.

The product is shown in the upper trace in Fig. 6.56 with the capacitor voltage as a time reference in the lower trace. For this, the PM 3265 oscilloscope is switched in the display mode MULTIPLY AND B, simply by depressing the two relevant pushbuttons simultaneously. During that time the voltage goes down, and as a consequence the current in Fig. 6.55 is negative and the displayed power is negative.

Summarizing, it could be said that the display of a negative product on the screen indicates that one of the factors of the product has the opposite sign to what was called positive.

As the multiplying circuit in the PM 3265 oscilloscope is a four-quadrant multiplier, both factors of the product may be negative for a positive product on the screen. For this reason it is very handy that one of the factors can be displayed simultaneously with the product. If the other factor is to be displayed along with the product, the connections to the Y_A and Y_B input terminals of the oscilloscope must be interchanged.

Another demonstration is the display of power, where the voltage and current are 90° out of phase. It is known that the average power consumption in an impedance at which the voltage is, for example, $e = E \sin \omega t$, and the current through it is $i = I \sin (\omega t + \varphi)$, is given by EI cos φ. In the case of $\varphi = 90°$, this results in no consumption because cos 90° = 0. But this is the power averaged over an integer number of periods.

This effect is demonstrated in Figs. 6.57 and 6.58. If in Fig. 6.57 the lower trace represents $e = E \sin \omega t$, then the upper trace may be $i = I \sin (\omega t + 90°) = I \cos \omega t$. Suppose that $E = 1$ V and $I = 1$ A and both are represented on the screen with 1 division amplitude (2 divisions peak-to-

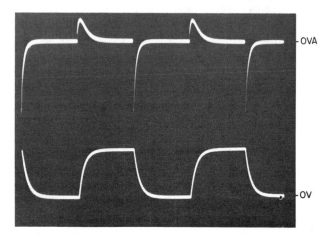

Fig. 6.56 (Upper trace) Product of both traces in Fig. 6.55. (Lower trace) voltage across a capacitor (as in Fig. 6.55).

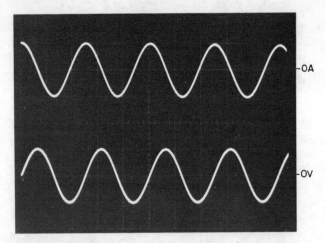

Fig. 6.57 (Upper trace) cos ωt and (lower trace) sin ωt.

Fig. 6.58 (Upper trace) $\frac{1}{2}$ sin $2\omega t$ = sin $\omega t \cdot$ cos ωt. (Lower trace) sin ωt.

peak). Then the upper trace in Fig. 6.57 is i = cos ωt, and the lower trace e = sin ωt. This can be observed best on the left-hand side of the screen. The upper trace in Fig. 6.58 shows the product

$$p = \cos \omega t \cdot \sin \omega t$$

$$= \tfrac{1}{2} \sin 2\omega t$$

which is also indicated best on the left-hand side of the screen, at the beginning of the upper trace. The lower trace still shows sin ωt.

As can be observed from the screen, the *average value* of the product is indeed zero, but the instantaneous value varies around the zero level with double the frequency and half the amplitude.

If the phase shift φ is not 90° (or 270°), but in general φ, the *average level* of the product will be $\frac{1}{2} \cos \varphi$. For example, if $\varphi = 0$, then the average level is $\frac{1}{2} \cos 0 = \frac{1}{2}$, in accordance with $\sin^2 \varphi t = \frac{1}{2} - \frac{1}{2} \cos 2\omega t$. Note that the *average value* of $\cos 2\omega t$ is again zero.

Transient Response Power in Switching Transistor

Switching transistors may be used to discharge a capacitor. When the capacitor is bypassed by the collector and emitter connections of a switching transistor, the former can be short-circuited by switching the transistor to its conducting state at the base. As the collector-emitter voltage is not zero in its conducting state, a discharge current of the capacitor will cause some dissipation in the transistor. This dissipation power is measured with the aid of the multiplier oscilloscope. Apart from the circuit under test, no other equipment is required other than the oscilloscope itself, because use is made of the probe calibration-voltage output and the probe supply-voltage output—both available on the oscilloscope front panel.

Measuring Procedure

Equipment Required:

- 1 Multiplier oscilloscope
- Test circuit (see Fig. 6.59)
- Measuring cables

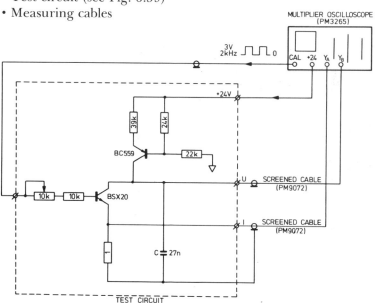

Fig. 6.59 A test setup for measuring transient response power in a transistor with the aid of a multiplier oscilloscope.

Initial Setup

SET THE OSCILLOSCOPE TO:

AMPL/DIV Y_A: 50 mV
AMPL/DIV Y_B: 2 V
Input couplings (both): DC
TIME/DIV MTB: 0.2 ms
TIME/DIV DTB: 10 μs
DTB multiplier: adjusted
TRIG source MTB: Y_B

TRIG slope MTB: −
TRIG coupling MTB: DC
TRIG mode MTB: AUTO
TRIG level MTB: adjusted
TRIG mode DTB: start
Channel switch: ALT
Display mode: ALT TB

When the calibrating voltage is 0 V, the transistor BSX20 is switched off (nonconducting). Capacitor C is charged via the current source BC 559. When the calibration voltage goes high to +3 V, the BSX20 is switched on and the capacitor discharges rapidly (see the second trace from the bottom in Fig. 6.60). The top trace shows the voltage across the 1-Ω emitter resistor, representing the collector current. Because of the ALTERNATE TIMEBASE mode, the enlarged transients are displayed simultaneously in the second trace from the top and the bottom traces (see Sec. 2.14).

As long as the calibration voltage remains high, the charging current flows through the BSX20. Only when this voltage drops to 0 V (and the capacitor starts to charge) will the current through the BSX20 be zero, as will the current through the 1-Ω emitter resistor. This can be noticed in the top trace in Fig. 6.60.

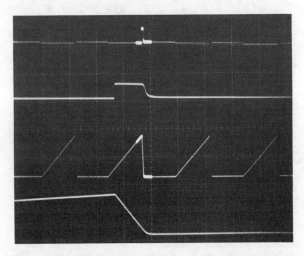

Fig. 6.60 The second trace from the bottom shows charging and discharging voltage of capacitor. The top trace represents the current.

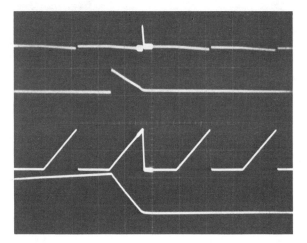

Fig. 6.61 The top trace represents power consumption in transistor BSX20, 100 mV/div (Y_A = 50 mA/div and Y_B = 2 V/div).

Next the channel switch is set to MULTIPLIER AND B. Now the top trace displays the power peaks during the transient (second trace enlarged by DTB) (see Fig. 6.61). As the voltage at channel Y_A is measured across 1 Ω, a 50 mV/div setting is actually 50 mA/div. Channel Y_B is set to 2 V/div, resulting in a power per division reading in the top trace of 100 mW/div. In the development of digital circuits, this kind of measurement is useful in checking the power consumption.

Power Consumption during the Recovery Time of Diodes

The recovery time of a diode when the supplied voltage is reversed depends upon the charge distribution in the PN junction. The diode current in the forward direction will provide a certain amount of stored excess charge in the PN junction. When the voltage across the diode is reversed, this charge must be removed before the diode can cease conducting, which is often called the "hole storage effect." During this time a reverse current is flowing. The effects of reversing voltages are demonstrated here by means of 2 diodes, a small one (OA 200) and a power diode (BY 127).

Measuring Procedure

Equipment Required:

- 1 Multiplier oscilloscope
- 1 Diode
- 1 Power diode

- 1 Pulse generator
- 1 50-Ω termination resistor
- Measuring cables

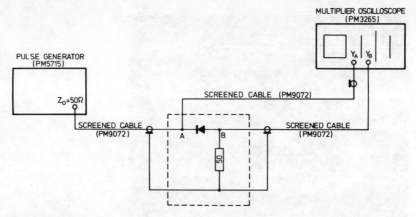

Fig. 6.62 Power measurement of a switching diode.

Initial Setup

SET THE PULSE GENERATOR TO
(PM 5715):

SET THE OSCILLOSCOPE TO:

REP. TIME: $10\ \mu s$ range
MODE: $T/2$, square
T_r and T_f: 6–100 ns range
DC offset: -3 V
AMPL: 5 V

AMPL/DIV Y_A: 2 V
AMPL/DIV Y_B: 1 V
Input couplings both: DC
TIME/DIV MTB: 5 μs
DTB: OFF
TRIG source MTB: Y_A
TRIG slope MTB: +
TRIG coupling MTB: DC
TRIG mode MTB: AUTO
TRIG level MTB: adjusted
Channel switch: ALT
Display mode: ALT

The display obtained from the small diode is shown in Fig. 6.63. The diode is conducting just before the start of the trace. Triggering occurs at the transient where the diode is reverse-biased. The upper trace shows the supplied voltage (point A in Fig. 6.62); the lower trace shows the current (point B in Fig. 6.62). As can be seen from the photograph, a reverse current is flowing for about 1 μs, after which the diode ceases conducting exponentially until zero current is reached. When the current is zero, the output voltage of the pulse generator is at its open emf level, about 1 division, or 2 V.

When the diode is next conducting, the excess charge in the PN junction is built up first (exponentially) before normal conducting starts. The power involved during the recovery time can be studied by operating the oscilloscope in its MULTIPLY mode (see Fig. 6.64). The upper trace shows the product $Y_A \times Y_B$ (power); the lower trace still shows the current, as in Fig. 6.63. For the power (upper trace) the horizontal center axis is the zero level. When the current is zero, the power is zero also, but during the recovery time some power is consumed by the diode. During the conducting state, the power consumption is at maximum level.

As can be seen from Fig. 6.64 the power consumption during the recovery time is small compared to that of the conducting state. This is not the case with power diodes, as can be seen in Fig. 6.65. In a multi-exposed photograph, from top to bottom, the current, voltage, and power

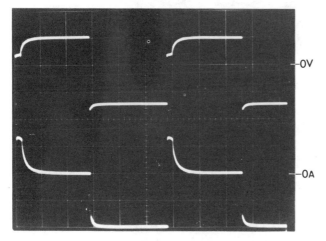

Fig. 6.63 The voltage across (upper) and current through (lower) a small diode (OA 200). TIME/DIV = 5 μs.

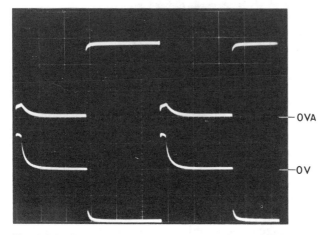

Fig. 6.64 Power consumption in (upper) and current through (lower) a small diode (OA 200). TIME/DIV = 5 μs.

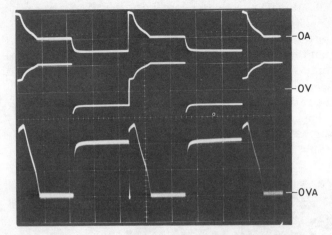

Fig. 6.65 From top to bottom; current, voltage, and power during the recovery time of a power diode (BY 127). TIME/DIV = 20 μs.

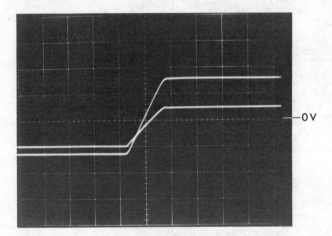

Fig. 6.66 Explanation of negative product during the transient in Fig. 6.65. The current (bigger step) is already positive (= above midscale), while the voltage is still negative. TIME/DIV = 0.05 μs.

are displayed. The time scale is now 20 μs/div; thus the recovery time can be seen to last much longer. The hole storage effect now lasts about 4 μs before recovery starts and ends at zero current.

It can be observed, indeed, that the power consumption (lower trace) during the recovery time is not small compared to the conducting state. When the reverse voltage is increased to the maximum permissible voltage for the BY 127 (a couple of hundred volts), the recovery power is even larger compared to that of the conducting state.

During the switching transient to the reverse state, it can be seen from Fig. 6.65 that the product is even slightly negative. This is explained with the aid of Fig. 6.66. In this picture the transient is enlarged by the DTB. The time scale is now 0.05 μs/div. The zero level for both the current and the voltage is centered at the horizontal center axis of the screen. Around the vertical axis the current is already positive (bigger step), while the voltage is still negative. Hence the product is negative, if only by a very small amount. This effect is influenced by varying the rise time T_r of the pulse generator.

6.4 STORAGE APPLICATIONS

Displaying the Bandpass Curve of a Filter

Frequently, the sweep speed (frequency increment per unit time) cannot be more than a few frequency octaves per second, because the filter under test needs time to respond. When displayed on a normal CRT, the filter characteristics cannot be observed from the screen while sweeping through the bandpass of interest at a sweep rate of a few sweeps per second. For this purpose a storage tube is very helpful, either in its variable-persistence mode or in its storage mode with a single sweep.

The following setup shows a measuring example in which a double-T filter is tested.

Measuring Procedure

Equipment Required:

• 1 Sweep generator (1 Hz–1 MHz)
• 1 Double-T filter (see Fig. 6.67)
• 1 Storage oscilloscope
• Measuring cables

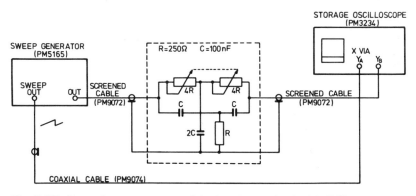

Fig. 6.67 Dynamic measurement of the bandpass of a double-T filter.

Initial Setup

SET THE (PM 5165) SWEEP
GENERATOR TO:

Upper frequency f_H: 100 kHz
Lower frequency f_L: 10 Hz
Sweep period time: 7s
Sweep control: CONT
Output waveform: SINE
Amplitude: 3 V_{pp}

SET THE (PM 3234) STORAGE
SCOPE TO:

TIME/DIV: X via Y_A
AMPL/DIV Y_A: 0.2V
AMPL/DIV variable: adjusted
AMPL/DIV Y_B: 20 mV
Storage mode: store

A repetitive waveform may appear as shown in Fig. 6.68. The Philips sweep generator PM 5156 has the facility to set the upper frequency f_H. The output of the SWEEP OUT is then 0 V and the vertical trace on the screen is adjusted on the right-hand side of the screen with the X POSITION control. Additionally, the lower frequency f_L is set. With the Y_A amplitude control the vertical trace is adjusted on the left-hand side of the screen so that a convenient frequency scale is obtained along the horizontal axis.

The example in Fig. 6.68 is chosen for 2 divisions per decade. Thus the left-hand side of the curve is 10 Hz; 2 divisions to the right, $10 \times 10 = 100$ Hz; 2 divisions further, $10 \times 100 = 1000$ Hz; etc. Now the dip in the bandpass curve of the double-T filter in Fig. 6.67 may be determined to be about 2 kHz. It must be noted here that the frequency scale is *logarithmic*.

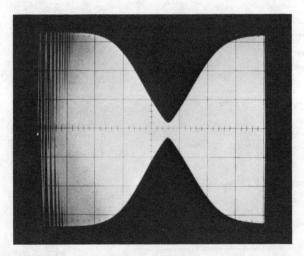

Fig. 6.68 The bandpass of a double-T filter. The frequency horizontal scale is 1 decade/2 divisions, covering 10 Hz to 100 kHz from left to right.

Bumping Time of Relay Contacts

It is assumed that, if a relay contact is closed, the switching action takes no time. Due to the switch action, the arrival of one contact point at the place of the other causes bouncing. This results in several openings and closings of the contact. The time taken for the contacts to finally close after the first bounce is called the *bumping time.*

Measuring Procedure

Equipment Required:

- 1 Storage oscilloscope
- 1 Relay
- 1 Power supply
- 1 Switch (single pole)
- Measuring cables

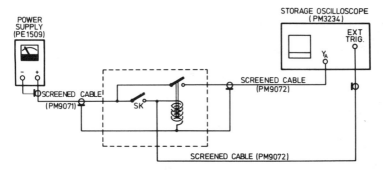

Fig. 6.69 Measuring the bounce of a relay contact.

Initial Setup

SET THE OSCILLOSCOPE TO:

AMPL/DIV Y_A: 2 V
TIME/DIV: 2 ms   TRIG coupling: DC
x5 MAGN: ON   TRIG slope: +
TRIG mode: SINGLE SWEEP   TRIG level: adjusted
TRIG source: EXT   Storage mode: VAR. PERS

The measuring procedure is very simple. When switch Sk is closed, the sweep is started after being SET READY. Then the bouncing action starts and is displayed as in Fig. 6.70. In order to obtain the bumping time in the middle of the screen, the 5X time-base magnifier is operated so that the desired picture can be displayed with the X POSITION control.

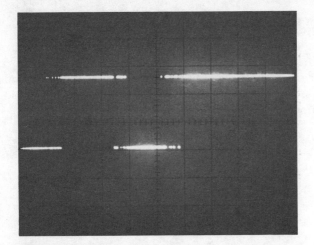

Fig. 6.70 Bumping time of a relay. TIME/DIV = 2 ms, TB MAGN X5 operated.

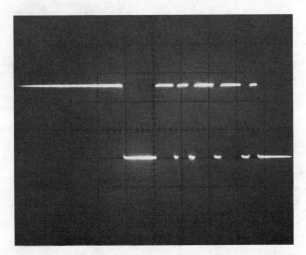

Fig. 6.71 Detailed view of contact bouncing. TIME/ DIV = 0.2 ms, TB MAGN X5 operated.

In Fig. 6.70 the time scale is set in this way to 0.4 ms/div. As can be read from the photograph, the bumping time in this case lasts about 2 ms. A detailed view is obtained in another trial by setting the TIME/DIV switch to 0.2 ms and still operating the 5X time-base magnifier. The result is shown in Fig. 6.71.

Note It is supposed that switch *Sk* in Fig. 6.69 does not bounce, which is seldom true in practice. Therefore, the power-supply unit and switch *Sk* would be better replaced by a function generator. In this case the output voltage should be a square wave with a repetition rate set to about 1 to 30 Hz.

An *R-S* flipflop, for example, composed of two NAND gates, can be used as well to eliminate the bouncing effect of switch Sk. The flipflop is placed in series between the switch and the relay coil.

Measuring the Exposure Time of Camera Shutters

This is also a typical single-shot measurement suited for a storage oscilloscope. The camera shutter, being a mechanical device, normally possesses exposure times of maybe 0.001 s (or 1 ms) up to 1 s.

Measuring Procedure

Equipment Required:

- 1 Storage oscilloscope
- 1 Camera
- 1 Phototransistor
- 1 Resistor, 10 kΩ

- 1 Small lamp
- 1 Power supply
- Measuring cables

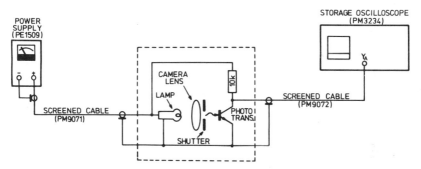

Fig. 6.72 Measuring the exposure times of a camera shutter.

Initial Setup

SET THE OSCILLOSCOPE TO:

AMP/DIV Y_A: 2 V
NORMAL INVERT: INVERT
TIME/DIV: 10 ms
TRIG mode: single
TRIG source: Y_A
TRIG coupling: DC
TRIG slope: −
TRIG level: adjusted
Storage mode: VAR.PERS.

SET EXPOSURE TIME OF THE CAMERA TO $\frac{1}{15}$ OR $\frac{1}{25}$ s:

POWER SUPPLY IS ADJUSTED TO THE LAMP USED.

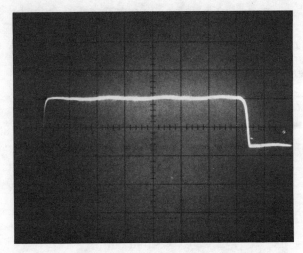

Fig. 6.73 The exposure time of camera shutter. TIME/DIV = 10 ms. Measured time is 74 ms for a camera shutter setting of $\frac{1}{15}$ s = 67 ms.

After the oscilloscope single trigger mode is set to READY, one operation of the camera shutter will cause an output pulse of the phototransistor. The picture may be similar to that shown in Fig. 6.73. The TIME/DIV switch was set to 10 ms. From the photograph an exposure time of 74 ms can be read. The camera was set to $1/15$ s = 67 ms. This means a deviation of about 10%, which is normal in cameras.

Some variation in the output voltage may be noticed. One period is 2 divisions = 20 ms which means a 50-Hz hum on the signal. Therefore, some care should be taken with this setup using short ground leads and screened cables.

SPECIFYING AN OSCILLOSCOPE

7.1 INTRODUCTION

Reading specifications is always difficult. The reader must know the exact meaning of each detail specified and must even be able to understand details that are not printed in the specifications. In this chapter some background information is given in a "Remarks" column to the relevant specification details. For example, the specifications of both a simple oscilloscope (Philips PM 3226) and a laboratory oscilloscope (Philips PM 3240) are listed on the following pages together with appropriate remarks. Where extra information is required for a proper explanation, reference is made to the Notes, which will be found following the specifications.

7.2 GENERAL INFORMATION ON THE PHILIPS PM 3226

Introduction

The 15-MHz portable dual-trace oscilloscope PM 3226 is a compact, lightweight instrument featuring simplicity of operation, for a wide range of use in servicing, research, and educational applications. Other features include provision for chopped or alternate display of Y signals, automatic triggering, mains triggering and triggering on the line and frame sync pulses of a television signal. The cathode-ray tube displays a useful screen area calibrated into 8 × 10 divisions by an external graticule.

All circuits are fully transistorized and mounted on printed circuit boards for ease of maintenance. The straightforward design and layout combines simple operation with a high degree of reliability.

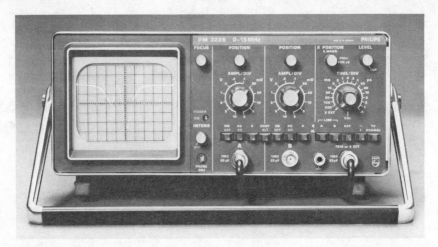

Fig. 7.1 Front view of a Philips PM 3226 oscilloscope.

Technical Data

General Instructions

Only properties expressed in numerical values, with tolerances stated, are guaranteed by the factory. Numerical values without tolerances are typical characteristics of an average instrument only.

Designation	Specification	Remarks
1. CATHODE-RAY TUBE		
Type	D10-160 GH	
Measuring area	8 × 10 divisions	1 division is not always 1 cm; here, 1 division = 0.8 cm
Screen type	P31 (GH) P7 (GM) optional	Refer to Table 3.1 for meaning P7-P31.
Acceleration voltage	1.5 kV	This order of magnitude means that a mono-accelerator tube has been used (Sec. 1.2)
Graticule	External, nonilluminated	Parallax in readout possible (Sec. 1.2)
Controls	Focus, intensity	

Designation	Specification	Remarks
2. VERTICAL AMPLIFIER		
Frequency range	dc, 0 Hz to 15 MHz (−3-dB bandwidth dc-coupled) ac, 2 Hz to 15 MHz (−3-dB bandwidth ac-coupled)	Refer to Note 7.1.
Rise time	25 ns	
Overshoot	≤3% (test pulse: 6-division amplitude, 3-ns rise time)	
Deflection coefficients	2 mV/div to 10 V/div in twelve calibrated steps in 1-2-5 sequence	Some manufacturers specify less bandwidth at higher sensitivities (= lower deflection coefficients). No continuous control
Maximum possible input voltage	±400 V (dc + ac peak) Resistant against non-repetitive surges of up to 1000 V	Hidden quality for circuit protection (attenuators and input amplifiers).
Vertical position range	±8 divisions	Here equivalent to 2 screen heights
Dynamic range	24 div. for sine-wave signals with frequencies of up to 3 MHz. ≥5 div. for sinewave signals of up to 15 MHz	3 screen heights; not always specified by every manufacturer.
Input impedance	1 MΩ ‖ 25 pF	Standard for most oscilloscopes (see Chap. 4).
Operating modes:		
Channel A	Channel A, ON/OFF push-button depressed	
Channel B	Channel B, ON/OFF push-button depressed	No possibility for ±B, thus neither $A − B$ (Sec. 2.4)
Channel $A + B$	Channels A and B, ON/OFF pushbutton depressed	
(electronically switched)	(chopped or alternate modes, pushbutton selected)	

Designation	Specification	Remarks
3. HORIZONTAL AMPLIFIER		
Frequency range	0 to 1 MHz (−3-dB band-width)	
Deflection coefficients	5 V/div at 1× magnification 1 V/div at 5× magnification	For x EXT input
Maximum permissible input voltage	±400 V (dc + ac peak). Resistant against non-repetitive surges of up to 1000 V	See Vertical Amplifier.
Input impedance	1 MΩ ‖ 25 pF	Standard. For possibility of using probe.
4. TIME BASE		
Time coefficients	0.2 s/div to 0.5 μs/div in 18 calibrated steps in 1-2-5. sequence. Uncalibrated continuous control 1:≤2.5	Related to bandwidth (15 MHz). Together with time-base magnifier (Expansion) 1.5 sine waves per division at 15 MHz.
Coefficient error	5%	$\frac{1}{2}$ division at f.s.d.
Expansion	×5, 1 calibrated step	
Additional error	<2%	Together with time-base error: 0.7 divisions
5. TRIGGERING		
Sources	Internal External Line	Channel A or B
Trigger sensitivity	Internal: Level −0.8 div at 100 kHz <1.2 div at 15 MHz Top −4 div at 15 MHz TV −1.0 div for line or frame sync pulses	Note: Internal specified in divs, External in volts

Designation	Specification	Remarks
	External: Level −0.7 V at 100 kHz ≤1 V at 15 MHz	
	Top −3 V at 15 MHz	
	TV −1.0 V for line or frame sync pulses	Thus standard in TV signals
Input impedance	1 MΩ ‖ 25 pF.	Standard
Maximum permissible input voltage	±400 V (dc + ac peak). Resistant against non-repetitive surges of up to 1000 V.	See Vertical Amplifier.
Trigger mode	Time-base generator runs free in absence of trigger signal. a. Trigger level adjustable over 12 divisions, or 12 V. Lowest triggerable frequency for sine waves = 10 Hz. b. Top	AUTO circuit built-in (See Sec. 2.10)
Trigger slope	+ or −	
Triggering with TV signals	Frame (coupled with positions 5 to 200 ms/div) Line (coupled with positions 2 ms/div to 0.5 μs/div)	
Probe adjustment	Contact point available at front panel.	

6. ENVIRONMENTAL CONDITIONS

Temperature
   Reference value   23°C
   Nominal operating
     temperature
     range   +5 to +40°C

Designation	Specification	Remarks
Operating temperature range limits	−10 and +55°C	
Temperature range for storage and transport	−40 to +70°C	Some specification points are limited with respect to the nominal operating temperature range.

7. OPERATING POSITION

Any

8. SUPPLY VOLTAGES

110, 127, 220, and 240 V
ac ± 10% (46 to 60 Hz)

9. MECHANICAL DATA

Height	140 mm, incl. feet and handle
Width	305 mm, incl. handle
Length	320 mm, incl. front cover
Weight	4.5 kg

10. COOLING

Natural convection

7.3 GENERAL INFORMATION ON THE PHILIPS PM 3240

Introduction

The PM 3240 portable hf oscilloscope enables the measurement of signals at a high sensitivity (5 mV/div) over a large bandwidth (50 MHz). There is a wide choice of display possibilities, such as one channel, two channels alternately or chopped, two channels added, with normal and inverted position for one input signal, and a main and delayed time base.

The PM 3240 oscilloscope features a tapless power supply with low dissipation. This power supply works on any ac mains voltage between 90 and 264 V, or any dc voltage between 90 and 200 V, thus obviating the need for adjusting the instrument to the local mains voltage. All these features make the oscilloscope suitable for a wide variety of applications.

Fig. 7.2 Front view of a Philips PM 3240 oscilloscope.

Characteristics

This specification is valid after the instrument has warmed up for 15 minutes. Properties expressed in numerical values with tolerances stated are guaranteed by the manufacturer. Numerical values without tolerances are typical and represent the characteristics of an average instrument.

Note: Generally for the more sophisticated oscilloscopes additional information is given, particularly with regard to the conditions under which the specifications are valid.

Designation	Specification	Additional information	Remarks
1. CRT			
Type	Philips D14.125 GH/08	Rectangular tube face, mesh type, postaccelerator, metal-backed phosphor	
Measuring area	80 × 100 mm		
Screen type	P31 (GH) phosphor	P11 (BE) and P7 (GM) phosphor optional	Compare with PM 3226

Designation	Specification	Additional information	Remarks
Photographic writing speed	>750 cm/μs	Measured with Steinheil Oscillophot M5 camera. Aperture: 1:1.2 Object-to-image ratio: 1:0.5 Film: Polaroid 410 (10000 ASA) No prefogging Phosphor type P31 (GH)	>0.75 cm/ns, or 1.33 ns/cm (ns/division) Refer to Sec. 1.2.
Total acceleration voltage	10 kV		PDA system (Sec. 1.2)
Graticule	Internal	Continuously variable illumination	
Engravings	Centimeter divisions with subdivisions of 2 mm along the central axes. Dotted lines indicate 10% and 90% of measuring lattice for measurement of rise times.		

2. VERTICAL, OR Y, AXIS

2.1. Response

Frequency range	dc to 50 MHz	−3-dB bandwidth dc-coupled	Refer to Note 7.1.
	10 Hz to 50 MHz	−3-dB bandwidth ac-coupled	
Rise time	≈7 ns		
Overshoot	±2%	Measured with a test pulse of 6 div; rise time, 2 ns; frequency, 1 MHz.	

Designation	Specification	Additional information	Remarks
2.2. Deflection coefficients	5 mV/div to 2 V/div	Nine calibrated positions in 1-2-5 sequence. Uncalibrated continuous control 1 : ≥2.5.	
2.3. Error limit	±3%		
2.4. Max. permissible input voltage	±400 V	dc + ac peak. Up to 20-mV position of input attenuator derating at frequencies over 500 kHz.	Refer to PM 3226.
2.5. Instability of the spot position			
DC drift	<0.3 div/h	At 20°C in position 5 mV/div	
Temperature drift	<60 μV/°C	Typical value	Typical values are mean values averaged over many instruments. No guarantee of the maximum value is given.
2.6. Maximum deflection			
Undistorted	24 divisions	For sine waves up to 15 MHz	
	≥6 divisions	For sine waves up to 50 MHz	
Shift range	16 divisions	8 divisions each in topward and downward direction reckoned from the central horizontal graticule line	
2.7. Input impedance	1 MΩ ‖ 15 pF		Standard

Designation	Specification	Additional information	Remarks
2.8. Input RC time	≈22 ms	Coupling switch to ac	Refer to Sec. 2.1.
2.9. Visible signal delay	Approximately 20 ns		See Fig. 2.8.
2.10. Display modes	Channel A only Channel $\pm B$ only Channels A and $\pm B$ chopped Channels A and $\pm B$ alternate Channels A and $\pm B$ added		Refer to Secs. 2.3 and 2.4.
2.11. Chopper frequency	1 MHz		

3. HORIZONTAL, OR X, AXIS

Display modes	Main time base Main time base intensified by delayed time base Delayed time base		Refer to Sec. 2.14.
	X-Y operation	X deflection by: Channel A signal Channel B signal Signal applied to EXT connector of main time base Mains frequency	

4. MAIN TIME BASE

4.1. Operation	Automatic	Possibility of automatic free-running in the absence of triggering signals	Refer to Sec. 2.10.
	Triggered single shot		
4.2. Time co-efficients	0.5 s/div to 50 ns/div	Twenty-two calibrated positions in 1-2-5 sequence.	Related to bandwidth of 50 MHz

Designation	Specification	Additional information	Remarks
		Uncalibrated continuous control 1: ≥2.5 between the steps.	
4.3. Coefficient error	±3%	+5 to +40°C Sweep accuracy in positions 0.5 and 0.2 s/div and 0.1 and 0.05 μs/div.	
4.4. Expansion Magnification	5×	Switched, calibrated	
Additional error	±2%		Together with time-base error of ±5%
Max. effective time coefficient	10 ns/div		

5. DELAYED TIME BASE

5.1. Operation	Delayed time base starts at option either immediately after the delay time, or is triggerable after the delay time.		Refer to Sec. 2.15.
5.2. Time coefficient	1 ms/div to 50 ns/div	Fourteen calibrated positions in 1-2-5 sequence. Uncalibrated continuous control; 1: ≥2.5 between the steps	
5.3. Coefficient error	±3%	+5 to +40°C Sweep accuracy 5% in positions 0.1 and 0.05 μs/div	

Designation	Specification	Additional information	Remarks
5.4. Delay Time	Continuously variable between approx. 0× and 10× the time coefficient of the main time base		
5.5. Delay-time jitter	<1:20,000		Mainly caused by comparator (irregularities in power supply) in Fig. 2.24 and only visible in START mode of DTB (see Sec. 2.15)

6. X DEFLECTION
X deflection
via channel Y_A
or Y_B

Designation	Specification	Additional information	Remarks
6.1. Deflection coefficient	5 mV/div to 2 V/div	Uncalibrated continuous control 2.5:1	
6.2. Coefficient error	±10%		
6.3. Bandwidth	0 to 1 MHz	−3-dB bandwidth over 8 div	
6.4. Input impedance	1 MΩ ‖ 15 pF		Standard
6.5. Phase difference	≤3° at 100 kHz		Refer to Note 7.2.
External X deflection via EXT socket			
6.6. Deflection coefficient	≤450 mV/div	Typical value 300 mV/div	Typical values are mean values averaged over many instruments. No guarantee of the maximum value is given.

Designation	Specification	Additional information	Remarks
6.7. Band-width	0 to 1 MHz	−3-dB bandwidth over 8 div	
6.8. Input character-istics	Identical to *Y* channels		
6.9. Phase dif-ference	≤3° at 100 kHz		Refer to Note 7.2.

X deflection with internal voltage at mains frequency
The deflection depends on the mains voltage and has been factory-adjusted to 8 divisions at a mains voltage of 220 V.

7. TRIGGERING OF THE MAIN TIME BASE

Designation	Specification	Additional information	Remarks
7.1. Source	Internal from channel *A* Internal from channel *B* Internal from mains External source	Internally adjustable for different mains voltages	Refer to Sec. 2.6.
7.2. Mode	Automatic	Automatic free-run of the time-base generator approx. 100 ms after disappearance of the trigger signal.	
	Manual level Single sweep		
7.3. Slope	+ or −		
7.4. Sensitivity	Internal ≤0.5 divisions External ≤150 mV	Typical ⅓ div Typical 100 mV	
7.5. Filter bandwidth of trigger coupling	dc:0 to 50 MHz lf:0 to 50 kHz lf:10 Hz to 50 kHz hf:50 kHz to maximum	Typical −15-dB bandwidth −3 dB, internal −3 dB, external −3 dB, both internal and external	Refer to Sec. 2.7.

Designation	Specification	Additional information	Remarks
7.6. Level range			
Internal triggering	≥16 divisions	Typical 24 divisions	
External triggering	≥4.8 V	Typical 7.2 V	
7.7. Input characteristics	Identical to Y channels		

8. TRIGGERING OF THE DELAYED TIME BASE

8.1. Source	Internal from channel A Internal from channel B External		

Other characteristics are identical to those under Triggering of the Main Time Base.

9. CALIBRATION UNIT

Designation	Specification	Additional information	Remarks
9.1. Output voltage	3 V peak-to-peak		
9.2. Output current	6 mA		Refer to Sec. 4.2.
9.3. Error limit	±1%	Both voltage and current	For calibrating current probe, refer to Sec. 4.4.
9.4. Frequency	2 kHz ± 2%		
9.5. Protection	The output is protected against continuous short circuits.		

10. POWER

Designation	Specification	Additional information	Remarks
10.1. Mains voltages	Any voltage between 100 and 240 V ± 10% in one range (ac)	Any voltage between 90 and 200 V dc.	

Designation	Specification	Additional information	Remarks
10.2. Mains frequency	46 to 440 Hz, or dc		
10.3. Power consumption	23 W		

11. ENVIRONMENTAL CAPABILITIES

The environmental data is valid only if the instrument is checked in accordance with the official checking procedure. Details on these procedures and failure criteria are supplied on request by the Philips organisation in your country, or by N. V. Philips' Gloeilampen-fabrieken, Test and Measuring Department, Eindhoven, Holland.

Designation	Specification	Additional information	Remarks
11.1. Ambient temperature	+5 to +40°C	Rated range of use	
	−10 to +55°C	Limit range of operation	
	−40 to +70°C	Storage and transport conditions	
11.2. Altitude	5000 m	Operating	
	15,000 m	Not operating	
11.3. Humidity	The instrument meets the requirements of the IEC 68 Db recommendations		
11.4. Bump	1000 bumps of 10 g, $\frac{1}{2}$ sine, 6 ms in duration, in each of 3 directions.		Refer to Note 7.3.
11.5. Vibration	30 minutes in each of three directions, 10 to 150 Hz; 0.7 mm peak-to-peak and 5 g max. acceleration.		
11.6. Recovery time	30 minutes for normal operation	Coming from −10 and going to +20°C at 60% relative humidity.	
11.7. Electromagnectic interference	The instrument meets the VDE, störgrad K, requirements.		Refer to Note 7.4.

Designation	Specification	Additional information	Remarks

12. MECHANICAL DATA

12.1. Dimensions	Length: 410 mm Width: 316 mm Height: 154 mm	Excl. controls, cover and feet.	
12.2. Weight	8.4 kg		

13. ACCESSORIES

13.1. Accessories delivered with the instrument
Contrast filter
Front cover with storage space
Collapsible viewing hood PM9366
Banana–BNC adapter PM9051
CAL terminal–BCN adapter
Manual

Remarks: Clear distinction must be made (also in advertisements) between accessories delivered with the instruments and optional accessories which must be ordered separately.

13.2. Optional accessories

PM 9335	Passive 1 : 1 probe
PM 9350	Passive 10 : 1 probe
PM 9347*	Active TV probe
PM 9353*	Active FET probe
PM 8960	Rack-mounting adaptor
PM 8971	Camera flange
PM 8980	Long viewing hood
PM 9280	Oscilloscope camera
M3 to M5	Oscilloscope camera range Steinheil Oscillophot

* Auxiliary probe power supply PM 9346 is necessary if these probes are to be used.

7.4 ADDITIONAL NOTES TO THE SPECIFICATIONS

Note 7.1

In the specification of an amplifier, the bandwidth or frequency response denotes one of the characteristics. A frequency-response curve may be as shown by the solid line in Fig. 7.3.

The vertical axis gives the amplification in dB on a logarithmic scale. 0 dB is a reference level mostly taken around a frequency of 10 kHz (1 kHz or 50 kHz). The bandwidth is then defined as the frequency where the amplitude of the output voltage is 3 dB down with respect to the reference. The magnitude of the input bandwidth is 10 MHz. (Note that this example concerns a dc-coupled amplifier, because the characteristic is flat from dc onwards.)

In order to improve the same amplifier's bandwidth, sometimes the amplification at 10 MHz is somewhat boosted (for example, by RC networks in feedback loops). This results in an extra gain of +3 dB at 10 MHz, while at the same time the −3-dB level is shifted to a higher frequency. And still one could speak about a 3-dB bandwidth without indicating, however, a + or − sign. In Fig. 7.3 this is indicated by the line of dashes; the −3-dB point is about at 50 MHz.

Thus, the higher frequencies are extra-amplified, a fact that cannot be learned from the −3-dB frequency specification only. But a result is that the display of a square-wave signal shows an overshoot (see pulse definitions in Sec. 5.2). This is why, apart from the bandwidth, the amount of overshoot is also specified in the charactcristics of an amplifier. Together these specifications give a fair idea of the amplifier's quality. The effect of the line of dashes in Fig. 7.3 is known as "peaking." An example is given in Fig. 7.4. The upper trace shows a proper display of a squarewave pulse, the lower trace shows overshoot.

Remark The vertical amplifier in an oscilloscope includes the attenuator; hence the overall response is also dependent upon the attenuator setting.

Note 7.2

In Sec. 6.2 some examples of *X-Y* measurements are given. In Note 7.1 the frequency characteristic of an amplifier is discussed. But besides the bandwidth of an amplifier, the "phase characteristic" also is of utmost

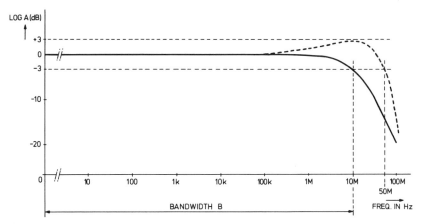

Fig. 7.3 Frequency characteristic of a dc-coupled, low-pass, broad-band amplifier.

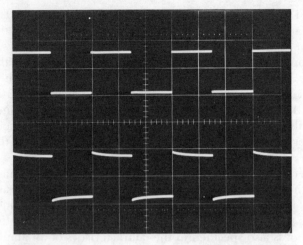

Fig. 7.4 Square wave, properly amplified (upper trace) and square wave amplified with hf peaking (lower trace).

importance. The phase characteristic shows the phase shift between the input and output signal as a function of the frequency. Mathematically, it can be proved that for an "ideal" amplifier response both the phase and the frequency characteristic must be flat. However, an "ideal" phase behavior is related to the frequency response.

For X-Y measurements the importance of the phase characteristics becomes obvious. If the X and Y amplification channels show different characteristics, then, without any phase shift in the signals to be measured (for example, the same signal), a phase shift is nevertheless displayed on the screen, usually at the higher frequencies. The reason for this is because the Y channel includes a delay line, whereas the X channel does not. Figure 7.5 shows the result for a 100-kHz sine wave in the X-Y mode of the Philips PM 3240 oscilloscope, with the same signal via Y_B for X deflection. The fraction of the Y axis cut off by the ellipsoid denotes $\sin \varphi$, with φ being the phase shift in degrees. From the photograph it can be learned that the phase shift between the X and Y channels at 100 kHz is about 1.5 degrees, which is within specification.

Note 7.3

Environmental testing is often referred to as testing an apparatus according to M_2C_1 or M_2C_2 rules. With few exceptions this statement is meaningless to the customer. In the case of the Philips PM 3240 oscilloscope, slightly more is specified, but still, item 11.3, which states that the requirements are fulfilling the IEC 68 Db recommendation, does not say very much. For this reason a glossary of operation conditions and test procedures for operating, storage, and handling is given in this Note.

What Does IEC Mean?

IEC stands for the International Electrotechnical Commission, which is affiliated to the International Organization for Standardization (ISO). The head office is in Geneva, Switzerland. The standards recommended by the IEC include:

• The way of specifying instruments
• Operating conditions
• Test procedures
• Safety requirements

These standards are important because every manufacturer who follows the IEC recommendations is specifying the same type of products in the same way, and this results in a greater degree of clarity for the customers.

Also, the Philips Product Division for Scientific and Industrial Equipment (S&I) follows the IEC recommendations, and a Quality Manual detailing the IEC requirements is binding within the S&I Division. A number of surveys and tables concerning environmental aspects selected from Part 5 of the Quality Manual are printed immediately following these Notes.

First, the *standard environmental conditions* are defined. Then, Tables 7.1 and 7.2 show the standard *climatic* and *mechanical* conditions for *operation*. The conditions for *storage* and *transport* are given in Table 7.3. A clear distinction must thus be made between operation and storage or transport.

The *tests,* intended to check *operation* during the specified environ-

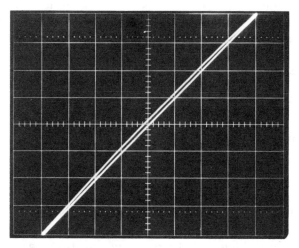

Fig. 7.5 *X-Y* display of 100-kHZ sine wave on a Philips PM 3240 oscilloscope, with *X* via Y_B.

mental conditions, are given in the survey in Table 7.4. Table 7.5 shows the tests for *transport, storage,* and *handling.* Reference is made in these tables to the corresponding IEC publication numbers.

Note 7.4

To prevent interference on receiving apparatus, for example, audio and TV receivers or computer systems, signals generated in the line supply and the radiated electromagnetic field of radio frequency from electrical equipment may not exceed certain limits. Here again, as described in Note 7.3, the IEC makes recommendations. For this a special committee of the IEC, the CISPR (International Special Committee on Radio Interference) has published a number of definitions concerning measuring sets and measurement procedures for the various types of interference-producing equipment.

Although the CISPR is an international committee, some countries have developed their own standards. In Germany the VDE committee (Verbandes Deutscher Elektrotechniker) has set its own requirements. The VDE requirements may not be incompatible with the IEC recommendations, and frequently reference is made to both (see Table 7.6).

Referring to item 11.7 in the PM 3240 specifications, it will be clear that the prime function of an oscilloscope is not to generate radiofrequency (rf) signals. The instrument only produces rf signals as a parasitic effect. Accordingly, the requirements must be read from Table 7.6, taken from the Philips S&I Quality Manual, Part 7.

Item 11.7 in the specification for the PM 3240 oscilloscope means that at 30-m distance the electromagnetic field due to parasitic radiation may not exceed a strength of 30 μV/m for frequencies between 10 kHz and 3000 GHz. The voltage that may be present at the "line terminal" (power cord) due to the instrument's power supply is given in the lowest graph shown in Fig. 7.7.

7.5 STANDARD ENVIRONMENTAL CONDITIONS

Introduction

For S&I products standard environmental conditions for operation are recommended for commonly existing applications. These conditions are based on IEC Publ. 359: *Expression of the functional performance of electronic measuring equipment.* This is intended, with other conditions, to unify methods used in making and clarifying statements on the functional performance of electronic measuring equipment.

Environmental condition		Application
Climatic	C1	Indoor
	C2	Partly protected area
	C3	Outdoor
Mechanical	M1	Buildings/laboratories, etc.
	M2	Vibrating structures
	M3	Vehicles
Supply	S1	Regulated supply
	S2	Public mains
	S3	Local generation
	S4	Battery supply

For each condition has to be specified:

• Reference condition   • Limit range of operation
• Rated range of use   • Storage and transport condition

Notes:

• Normally, apparatus intended for different conditions of *use* are subjected to the same climatic and mechanical conditions for *storage and transport.*

• During use apparatus may also be subjected to mechanical stresses, due to handling and local transport.

Definitions

C1 (Indoor) Environment normally found in locations destined for human work. At least some degree of heating, but no air conditioning. Located maximum at 2200 m. altitude.

C2 (partly protected) Wholly protected from rain, snow, hail, sand, and wind, but drip water may occur. No heating but some protection against lowest outdoor temperature. Protection against direct sunshine. Located maximum at 4000 m. altitude.

C3 (outdoor) No protection against open air influences other than built into the item. Located maximum at 4000 m altitude. Not located at area of extreme climatic conditions.

M1 (buildings/labs, etc.) (1) Equipment used stationary at locations with negligible vibration level; (2) equipment for which careful handling during operation and handling is specified.

M2 (vibrating structures) (1) Equipment used at locations with a perceptible vibration level as found in, e.g., factories, workshops, etc; (2) equipment subjected to normal handling during operation.

M3 (Vehicles) (1) Equipment used at locations with considerable vibrations as found on ships; on airplanes; on ground vehicles and in the neighborhood of heavy machinery; (2) equipment subjected to rough handling during operation.

Rated range of use (1) Conditions normally found during the use of the equipment; (2) conditions to which the operating error is related.

Limit range of operation Conditions which may be found during a relatively short period, during which operation outside specification is acceptable.

Reference conditions Conditions related to the intrinsic error and the influence factors.

Table 7.1 STANDARD CLIMATIC CONDITIONS FOR *OPERATION,* BASED ON IEC PUBL. 359

		C1 (indoor)	C2 (partly protected)	C3 (outdoor)
Temperature, °C	Rated	+5–+40 (+5–+55)	−10–+55	−25–+70
	Limit	Equal to the rated range of use unless otherwise stated		
Humidity, % RH		20–80	10–90	5–95
Liquid water		No	drip	Splash
Solar radiation		No	No	Corresp. to 70°C surface temp.
Dust		No	Light	Heavy
Condensation		No	Yes	Yes
Barometric pressure, kN/m² (mm Hg)		70.0–106.0 (525–800)	53.3–106.0 (400–800)	53.3–106.0 (400–800)
Air velocity, m/s		0–0.5	0–5	0–15

Table 7.2 STANDARD MECHANICAL CONDITIONS FOR *OPERATION*

	M1 (building/labs.)	M2 (vibrating structures)	M3 (vehicles)
Vibration (freq./displ./acc.) ("peak" values)	Negligible: <60 Hz/0.001 mm	Varies from: 5 Hz per 0.1 mm to 60 Hz per 0.01 mm	Max.: 100 Hz per 20 m/s²
Bump (acc./duration) ("peak" values)	Negligible: <2.5 m/s² per 60 ms	Varies from: 2.5 m/s² per 60 ms to 10 m/s² per 10 ms	Varies from: 20 m/s² per 20 ms to 200 m/s² per 2 ms

Notes:

1. The actual mechanical condition consists practically never of a sinusoidal or another deterministic influence. The actual mechanical stresses have mostly a random nature. The level specified for M2 and M3 present therefore not the actual condition but a level which is assumed to be sufficient to check if performance according to specification can be expected during the intended application.

2. The stress levels for M2 and M3 are S&I recommendations. The IEC levels are still under consideration.

Table 7.3 STANDARD STORAGE AND TRANSPORT CONDITIONS

Climatic conditions (for all classes)	
Temperature	-40 to $+70°C$
Humidity	5 to 95% R.H.
Barometric pressure	53.3 to 106.0 kN/m²
	(400 to 800 mm Hg)

Mechanical conditions (for all classes)	
Vibration:	
Frequencies	Up to 150 Hz
Acceleration	Max. 50 m/s²
Shock, varies from (acc./duration):	50 m/s² per 16 ms to 200 m/s² per 2 ms

NOTE: The actual mechanical stresses have mostly a random nature.

Table 7.4 SURVEY OF STANDARD *PERFORMANCE TESTS*

1. Climatic tests		Class		
		C1	**C2**	**C3**
1.1. Steady cold (see also IEC Publ. 68 test A)	Temperature, °C	+5	−10	−25
	Duration, h		2	
1.2. Steady dry heat (see also IEC Publ. 68 test B)	Temperature, °C	+40 (+55)*	+55	+70
	Duration, h		2	
1.3. Steady damp heat (see also IEC Publ. 68 test Ca)	Temperature, °C		+40	
	Humidity, % RH	80	90	95
	Duration, days	4	10	21

1.4. Condensation test: see IEC document 50 B (Germany) 139

1.5. Cycling dry temperature: under consideration

2. Mechanical tests		Class	
		M2	**M3**
2.1. Sinusoidal vibration (see also IEC Publ. 68 test Fc)	Frequency, Hz	10 to 55	10 to 150
	Amplitude	0.035 mm	0.15 mm per 20 m/s²†
	Direction	Normal use	
	Sweep rate	1 octave/minute	
	Number of sweeps	Sufficient for measurements (min. 4)	
2.2. Bump (see also IEC Publ. 68 test Eb)	Amplitude	10 m/s²	50 m/s²
	Pulse, half sine	6 ms	6 ms
	Direction	Normal use	
	Number	Sufficient for measurements (min. 1000)	

* +55°C for rack-mounted equipment.
† For mobile equipment the operational test M3 may also be performed at an amplitude of 3.5 mm and a maximum acceleration of 20 m/s², corresponding to a crossover frequency between 11 and 13 Hz.

Table 7.5 SURVEY OF TRANSPORT, STORAGE, AND HANDLING TESTS
(During transport and storage an item may be stressed by conditions exceeding the limit range of operation. During these conditions an item is not operating. Portable apparatus may be subjected to handling during operation. In that case they should not be damaged and remain safe.)

1. Climatic tests (for all classes)		
1.1. Steady cold (see also IEC Publ. 68 test A)	Temperature	−40°C
	Duration	72 h

Table 7.5 (continued)

1.2. Steady dry heat (see also IEC Publ. 68 test B)	Temperature	+70°C
	Duration	96 h
1.3. Cyclic damp heat (see also IEC Publ. 68 test Db)	Temperature	+25 to +40°C
	Humidity	95% RH*
	Number of 24-h cycles	21

2. Mechanical tests (for all classes)

2.1. Sinusoidal vibration (see also IEC Publ. 68 test Fc; Procedure B3)		
a. *Unpacked for equipment ≤30 kg*	Frequency	10 to 150 Hz
	Amplitude	0.35 mm per 50 m/s^2
	Sweep rate	1 octave/minute
	Direction	3 perpendicular
	Number of sweeps	4 per direction
b. *Unpacked for equipment >30 kg ≤ 100 kg*	Frequency	10 to 55 Hz
	Amplitude	0.15 mm
	Sweep rate	1 octave/minute
	Direction	3 perpendicular
	Number of sweeps	6 per direction
c. *Unpacked for equipment >100 kg:* Tests should be carried out on (functional) parts, corresponding to their weight.		
2.2. Bump (see also IEC Publ. test Eb)	Amplitude	100 m/s^2
a. *Unpacked for equipment ≤100 kg*	Pulse, half sine	6 ms
	Direction	3 perpendicular
	Number of bumps	1000 per direction
b. *Unpacked for equipment >100 kg:* Tests should be carried out on (functional) parts, corresponding to their weight.		
2.3. Rock test *Packed for equipment ≤50 kg*	Amplitude	7 mm
	Frequency	420 rpm
	Duration	10 min per face
2.4. Drop test *Packed for equipment ≤50 kg*	Number of droppings	6 droppings, 1 on each side
	Dropping height	(see Fig. 7.6)
2.5. Topple test *Packed for equipment >50 kg*		

Table 7.5 *(continued)*

		Class
		Portable M1
3. Handling test		**M2** **M3**
3.1. Drop test (see IEC Publ. 68-2-31, test Ec) *Unpacked*	Drop after tilting about each of the 4 bottom edges	25 mm 100 mm or 30 degrees, whichever is less severe

* Condensation should occur.

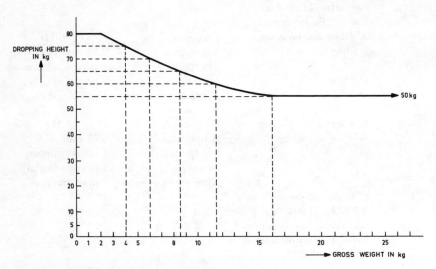

Fig. 7.6 Mechanical drop test (see Table 7.5, item 2.4).

7.6 RADIO FREQUENCY INTERFERENCE LIMITS

IEC/CISPR prepares technical recommendations for the maximum rf interference limits.

As radio frequencies (rf) are considered the frequencies in the range from 10 kHz to 3000 GHz.

Two categories of apparatus are distinguished:

• Apparatus intentionally using or generating rf: radio frequency equipment

• Apparatus producing rf as a parasitic effect

The limits may depend on the field of application of the apparatus.

Classification of ISM Radio Frequency Equipment

CISPR Recommendation No. 39 specifies limits for Industrial, Scientific, and Medical (ISM) radio frequency equipment.

Class I

• Equipment, manufactured in series, which meet the limits of Class I.

• The limits of Class I correspond to the limits of CISPR recommendation no. 39.

• Equipment meeting these limits may disturb rf communication under certain conditions.

• National authorities may impose administrative formalities for operation; for example, notification of operation by the user.

Class II

• Equipment, manufactured in series, which meet the limits of class II. The limits of class II are more stringent than the limits of class I.

• Equipment meeting these limits will generally not cause interference. National authorities refrain from administrative procedure for operation.

Table 7.6 LIMITING VALUES OF RADIATION (in μV/m)

| Frequency range, MHz | On a test site at a distance from the appliances of: | | | |
| | Class I | | Class II | |
	30 m	100 m	10 m	30 m
0.15 to 0.285	—	50	—	50
0.285 to 0.49	—	250	—	50
0.49 to 1.605	—	50	—	50
1.605 to 3.95	—	250	—	50
3.95 to 30	—	50	—	50
30 to 41	500	—	50	—
41 to 68	30	—	50	—
68 to 80	500	—	50	—
80 to 108	30	—	50	—
108 to 162	500	—	50	—
162 to 230	30	—	50	—
230 to 470	500	—	50	—
470 to 960	100	—	200	—
960 to 1000	500	—	200	—

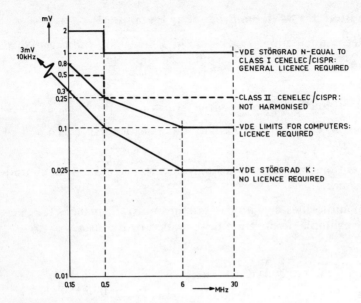

Fig. 7.7 Mains terminal voltage limits.

Other Equipment

Equipment other than class I and class II will generally be subject to national regulations. ISM equipment of this class consist generally of large equipment which has to be tested at the location of operation.

Note: For S & I radio frequency equipment it is recommended that the requirements of class II be met. If this is not feasible, the requirements of class I (CISPR 39/1) shall be met.

Limits in Germany for ISM Radio Frequency Equipment

1. Mains terminal voltage limits (see Figure 7.7)
2. Radiation

　　a. VDE störgrad N—equal to CENELEC/CISPR
　　　Class I:
　　　General license required.

　　b. VDE limits for computers:
　　　10 kHz–30 MHz: 50 μV/m at 30 m distance
　　　>30 MHz　　　: 30 μV/m at 10 m distance
　　　License required.

　　c. VDE störgrad K:
　　　10 kHz to 3000 GHz: limit 3 μV/m at 30 m distance
　　　No license required.

ANSWERS TO EXERCISES

CHAPTER 1

1. a. (A) T_{rep} = 25 ms, so $N = f = 1/T_{rep}$ = 40 Hz

   b. (B) $\dfrac{25 \text{ ms}}{100}$ = 0.25 ms. (C) is also correct, 0.25 ms = 250 μs

   c. (B) Only pulse b is affected, because the start of the sweep is determined by pulse a.

2. (C) Next sweep starts on pulse 3 as can be seen from the timing diagram. A nonrepetitive display will be the result.

3. a. (C) The screen has 10 horizontal divisions, thus

$$n \approx \frac{1 \text{ ms}}{10 \times 0.5 \ \mu s} \approx 200:1$$

   b. (A) Because, for most of the time, the spot is at the start of the sweep.

4. (A) Because the deflection sensitivity is increased. (C) is also correct. Post-deflection acceleration (PDA) is needed to increase the brightness, but the deflection sensitivity (DS) decreases. The use of the mesh restores the DS. The overall result then is the same DS but with PDA, and thus with increased brightness.

CHAPTER 2

1. (B) In the AUTO mode the time base will free run between triggers if the repetition rate is too low.

2. (C) With most oscilloscopes the trigger pick-off point is in front of the Y POSITION controls.

3. (C) A will prevent the trigger point from varying with the changes in the average value of the signal, and B because with a second cycle on the screen, the second cycle will be seen to have jitter.

4. (A) Refer to Fig. 2.10.

5. (B) Refer to Fig. 2.6.

6. (C) Refer to Fig. 2.21.

7. (C)

8. (B) C also; refer to Fig. 2.12.

9. (B) Refer to Fig. 2.23.

10. (C) Refer to Fig. 2.25.

11. (A) Refer to Fig. 2.28.

12. (B) Refer to Fig. 2.25.

13. (C) Delayed sweeps are only produced with main sweeps running.

(B) Only relevant with the DTB trigger circuit in the TRIG mode.

CHAPTER 3

1. (B)

2. (C)

3. (A and C) These answers are related by $B\tau_r = 0.35$.

4. (B)

5. (A)

6. (B) When a higher frequency is selected, double pictures or timing errors may occur (explained in detail in Sec. 5.8).

7. (B)

8. (C)

CHAPTER 4

1. (A) A is the best choice. B and C may also be good choices, but are not valid for all probes.

2. (C)

3.   (C)

4.   (B)

CHAPTER 5

1.   (B) Refer to Fig. 5.4.

2.   (B) The rise time follows from:

$$B\tau_r = 0.35$$

$$\tau_r = \frac{0.35}{10 \times 10^6} = 35 \text{ ns}$$

3.   (C) The rise time τ_0 of the oscilloscope follows from:

$$B\tau_0 = 0.35$$

$$\tau_0 = \frac{0.35}{120 \times 10^6} \approx 3 \text{ ns}$$

then (Sec. 5.4),

$$\tau_{st}^2 = \tau_s^2 - \tau_0^2 - \tau_{pr}^2$$

$$= 121 - 9 - 12.25$$

$$= 99.75$$

$$\tau_{st} = \sqrt{99.75} \approx 10 \text{ ns}$$

4.   (B) Refer to Fig. 5.8.

5.   (A) Refer to Sec. 5.6.

6.   (A) Refer to Figs. 5.27 and 5.28.

APPENDIX A
Glossary of Terms
in Oscilloscopy

The following glossary of terms reflects the usage of terms in this book and those commonly used on oscilloscopes, but may not reflect terms in general usage. Terms printed in **bold** letters in the definitions are themselves defined in the glossary.

A

Acceleration voltage The voltage with respect to the **cathode** of the **CRT,** that electrons have passed after **emission** and causes acceleration in the direction of the **screen.**

AC/DC input coupling With ac coupling a capacitor is switched between the input bus of the Y or **vertical channel** and the input circuit inside the **oscilloscope** in order to block dc components of the input signal. With dc coupling the capacitor is bypassed. [*Sec. 2.1*]

Active probe A **probe** by which signals are amplified. To be distinguished from a **passive probe.** [*Sec. 4.3*]

Add mode The ability to display the algebraic sum of two signals. [*Sec. 2.4*]

Alternate mode The means of display by which electronic switching between the **Y-input** signals is arranged such that one signal after the other is displayed in sequential **sweeps.** [*Secs. 2.2 and 3.3*]

Alternate time base Display of the **sweeps** of both the **main time base** and the **delayed time base** in an alternate way. [*Sec. 2.14*]

Aluminized layer A transparent aluminum layer internally deposited over the phosphor **screen** to avoid burning by the **beam** and to increase light output. In the **storage CRT** it is also used as a control electrode. [*Fig. 3.3*]

Anodes In a **CRT,** the tubular electrodes which are held at a positive potential to attract and accelerate the **electron beam. Focusing** of the **beam** is also caused by the anodes due to their mutual voltages. [*Fig. 1.2*]

Aquadag layer A conductive coating on the inside of the part of the **CRT** between the neck and the **screen.** [*Sec. 1.2*]

Attenuator An arrangement of resistors, capacitors, etc., which introduces a known attenuation of the input signal. [*Sec. 1.4*]

Auto triggering (1) **Trigger mode** in which a **sweep** is always initiated independent of the presence or absence of a **trigger signal** (auto-free-running mode). (2) Sometimes used instead of **automatic trigger level control.** [*Secs. 2.8 and 2.10*]

Automatic trigger-level control The **trigger mode** by which the control voltage for the **trigger level** setting is derived internally from the peak-to-peak value of the **trigger signal.** [*Fig. 2.15*]

B

Bandwidth In electronics the band of frequencies which can pass through an electrical or electronic circuit (amplifier, filter, etc.). Ideally, all frequencies within the bandwidth are passed with the same response (attenuation or amplification). Technically, the frequency response deviates between certain limits within the bandwidth (e.g., by 10% or 30%). In amplifiers the bandwidth is usually given by the frequency limits where the response is $1/\sqrt{2} \approx 0.7$ of the one at a reference frequency within the bandwidth. This may be also called the -3-dB bandwidth, because $20 \log 1/\sqrt{2} = -3$.

Beam See **electron beam.**

Bistable CRT A storage **CRT** that can display a stored pattern at only one brightness and has no **persistence** control. [*Sec. 3.1*]

Blanking The cutting off of the **electron beam** in a **CRT** by a voltage applied between the **cathode** and the **Wehnelt cylinder.** [*Sec. 1.2*]

Brightness See **intensity.**

C

Cable termination The termination of the end of a transmission line or cable by a resistor matched to the characteristic impedance of the cable. [*Figs. 5.7 and 5.8*]

Calibration generator The internal **square-wave** voltage generator in an **oscilloscope** (about 1 kHz) with an exact output amplitude, e.g., 3 V peak-to-peak $\pm 1\%$, for calibration checks and **probe adjustments.** [*Sec. 4.2 and Fig. 4.8*]

Cathode The part of the **electron gun** from which electrons are emitted by heating. [*Fig. 1.2*]

Cathode-ray tube An electronic tube in which a controllable **electron beam** is directed on to a phosphor **screen** to visualize a display by **phosphorescence.** [*Fig. 1.2*]

Channel switch An **electronic switch** which selects the display of the **Y-input** signals in either the **chopped mode,** or **alternate mode,** or selects only one signal to be displayed. If provision is made, one of the displayed signals might be the algebraic sum or product of two signals. [*Fig. 2.2*]

Chopped mode A means of display by which fast electronic channel switching (1 MHz) between the **Y-input** signals occurs, controlled by an internal free-running multivibrator with no frequency-relation to either of the signals. [*Secs. 2.2 and 3.3*]

Chopper frequency The frequency at which the electronic **channel switch** is operating in the **chopped mode.**

Coaxial cable A cable having a central conductor surrounded by an outer tubular conductor. The intervening dielectric may be air (with minimum insulating material) but in connection with **oscilloscopes** it is usually solid polyethylene.

Cold switching The operation of electronic functions (switching or continuous control) by means of dc voltages.

Collector mesh The mesh in a **variable-persistence storage CRT** which collects **flood electrons** repelled by the **storage layer.** [*Figs. 3.2 and 3.3*]

Collimator A thin metal layer vaporized on to the inside of the **storage CRT** cone and used as an electrode to control the cloud of **flood electrons.** [*Figs. 3.1 and 3.2*]

Common-mode rejection ratio The ratio of the **common-mode voltage** to the error voltage caused by it. [*Sec. 2.4*]

Common-mode voltage The voltage present in the same phase and amplitude at both signal-carrying leads of an electronic device (generator, amplifier) with respect to a zero or **ground** level. [*Sec. 2.4*]

Compact oscilloscope An **oscilloscope** mechanically composed into a single closed cabinet, as distinct from a **plug-in oscilloscope.**

Composite triggering A means of **triggering** where the **trigger source** is usually the output signal of the **channel switch.** [*Sec. 2.6 and Fig. 2.9*]

Control logic A **digital circuit** which can be set to control or to allow execution of certain operations in other **digital circuits.** [*Fig. 3.48*]

CRT See **cathode-ray tube.**

Current probe A **probe** designed to sense currents through electrical leads. [*Sec. 4.4*]

D

DC offset voltage The sustained deviation of a voltage from a reference or a zero voltage level. [*Fig. 5.2*]

Deflection coefficient The ratio of displacement of the **spot** on the screen to the input voltage at the **vertical (horizontal) channel,** expressed in volts per **division.** It can be varied by adjusting the settings of the **attenuators** (coarse, fine, or continuous). [*Chap. 7*]

Deflection plates Two pairs of plates each perpendicular to the other and located between the **electron gun** and the **screen** of a **CRT.** Used to deflect the **beam** in X and Y directions by applying voltages to each pair of plates. [*Fig. 1.2*]

Deflection sensitivity The ratio of displacement of the **spot** on the **screen** to the **deflection voltage,** expressed in **divisions** per volt. [*Sec. 1.2*]

Deflection voltage The voltage applied to the **deflection plates.**

Delay line A length of transmission cable purposely introduced in a signal path to obtain a time delay in the propagation of the signal created by the finite propagation velocity of the electrical signal along the cable. [*Sec. 2.5*]

Delay time An adjustable delay in time after which the **delayed time base** of an **oscilloscope** can be started following the start of the **main time base.** [*Sec. 2.13*]

Delay time multiplier A multiturn potentiometer situated on the **oscilloscope's** front panel. Its calibrated scale provides the factor by which the **time coefficient** of the **main time base** has to be multiplied to obtain the **delay time.** [*Sec. 2.13*]

Delayed sweep The sweep generated by the **delayed-time-base circuit.**

Delayed time base (**1**) A base for the scale of time of the **sweep** generated by the **delayed-time-base circuit.** (**2**) A frequently used abbreviation for **delayed-time-base circuit.**

Delayed-time-base circuit A second **time-base generator** which can be activated an adjustable time (**delay time**) after the start of the first or **main-time-base sweep.** [*Sec. 2.13*]

Delayed-time-base jitter Time **jitter** in the starting point of the **delayed sweep.**

Differential amplifier An amplifier with a 3-terminal input which amplifies only the voltage difference between the two ungrounded terminals. Voltages common to both ungrounded terminals are rejected. The output voltage may be present either with respect to ground (single ended out) or as a differential voltage; 3 terminals as at the input (differential out).

Differential mode (A − B or B − A) The display of a difference signal composed of two signals, each with respect to **ground.** One signal (B or A) is first inverted in polarity and then algebraically added to the other signal (A or B). [*Sec. 2.4*]

Digital circuit A circuit designed to operate with **digital signals.**

Digital delay The ability to start the **delayed-time-base sweep** after a preset number of **pulses** or signal periods digitally counted at its input. [*Fig. 3.3*]

Display-mode (**1**) For the **vertical channels** it is the way in which the **Y-input** signals may be displayed, for example, one signal only, or **alternate mode, chopped mode, add mode,** etc. (**2**) For the horizontal deflection it may be **main-time-base sweep** only, **main time base** intensified by **delayed time base, delayed time base** only, X-Y operation, etc.

Digital signal A signal which is only defined in either of two specified levels.

Distortion   The change of the original shape of a signal **waveform.**

Divisions   The distances between the cross lines on the **graticule.** [*Sec. 1.2*]

Double insulation   A combination of **functional insulation** and **supplementary insulation** to provide sufficient safety in case of a failure of the **functional insulation.**

Droop   A slight decay in the final amplitude of a **pulse voltage** after the **transition** has reached its desired level. [*Fig. 5.3*]

DTB   Abbreviation for **delayed time base.**

Dual-beam CRT   A term referring to both the **dual-gun CRT** and the **split-beam CRT.**

Dual-beam oscilloscope   An **oscilloscope** providing two traces on the **screen** by means of two simultaneous writing **beams.** [*Sec. 2.2*]

Dual-delayed time base   A facility to start the **DTB sweep** alternating after each **MTB sweep,** thereby allowing time-interval measurements. [*Sec. 2.17*]

Dual-gun CRT   A **CRT** possessing two **electron guns.**

Dual-trace oscilloscope   An **oscilloscope** providing two traces on the **screen** of a **single-gun CRT** by means of electronic switching. [*Sec. 2.2*]

Duty cycle   The ratio of the **pulse width** to the **pulse** repetition time. [*Fig. 5.4*]

Dynamic range   In **oscilloscopes** it is the undistorted deflection permitted by the Y-input amplifier, expressed in **divisions** because of the various possible settings of the **attenuator,** which influences the **deflection coefficient.** [*Chap. 7*]

E

Electron beam   The beam of electrons emitted by the **cathode** of the **electron gun** in a **CRT.** [*Fig. 1.2*]

Electron gun   The part of the **CRT** which furnishes a focused beam of electrons towards the **screen.** [*Fig. 1.2*]

Electronic switch   A device for opening or closing an electronic signal path by electronic means. In **oscilloscopes** it usually means the **channel switch.**

Emission   The release of electrons from parent atoms on absorption of energy. In a **CRT** arising from thermionic agitation by heating the **cathode.**

Erasure   The deliberate cancellation of the stored information in a **storage CRT.**

External triggering   The **triggering** by which a signal other than a **Y-input** signal is used as the **trigger source.** An extra input bus for the external **trigger signal** is provided on the front panel of the **oscilloscope.** [*Sec. 2.6*]

F

Fall time   The time taken for a pulse voltage to fall from 90 to 10% of the maximum amplitude. [*Fig. 5.2*]

FET probe   An **active** voltage **probe** with a miniature amplifier with field-effect transistor (FET) input built into the **probe tip**. [*Figs. 4.11 to 4.14*]

Floating measurements   The measurements by which the only galvanic contact between the measuring instrument and the device under test is made by the measuring leads. Of particular interest are cases where the galvanic insulation may be bypassed by means of the power line connections of both measuring instrument and device under test. [*Fig. 5.29*]

Flood electrons   The electrons coming from the **flood guns** in a **storage tube.** [*Fig. 3.5*]

Flood guns   Auxiliary **electron guns** in the **storage CRT** emitting a cloud of electrons, installed to visualize the stored pattern written on the **storage layer** by the **electron beam.** [*Fig. 3.5*]

Flood-system   The system in a storage CRT consisting of the **flood guns** and **collimator.**

Flyback   The part of the **sweep** during which the **sweep voltage** drops back to its initial level. Usually **blanking** is applied during flyback. [*Sec. 1.3*]

Focus   The point (on the **screen**) where the **electron beam** converges after having passed through the **focusing electrodes** of the **CRT.** [*Sec. 1.2*]

Focusing   The degree of convergence leading to the smallest diameter of the **spot** on the **screen.**

Focusing electrodes   The part of the **electron gun** by which the **electron beam** is focused on the **screen.** [*Fig. 1.2*]

Four-channel oscilloscope   An **oscilloscope** capable of displaying four simultaneous input signals. [*Sec. 3.3*]

Four-quadrant multiplier   An electronic multiplier circuit capable of handling every possible combination of polarities of the two input signals to be multiplied. To be distinguished from the two-quadrant multiplier where the polarities of the two input signals must be the same, i.e. either both positive or both negative. [*Fig. 3.32*]

Frequency range   In oscilloscopy it is the bandwidth of the **vertical channel.** [*Chap. 7*]

Functional insulation   The insulation necessary for the operation of electrical equipment and for basic protection against electric shock.

G

Gate   A circuit in digital electronics with more than one input terminal and only one output terminal. The signal condition (logic states 0 or 1) at the output is dependent on the mutual relationship of the input signal conditions (logic states 0 or 1). For example, the output of a multi-input gate is a logic 1 if, and only if, the state of all input signals is a logic 1. (AND gate).

Graticule A net of rectangular cross-lines permitting measurements to be taken from the **screen** either internally deposited on the **screen** or externally placed in front of the **CRT.** The distances between the cross-lines are the **divisions.** [*Sec. 1.2*]

Ground The common point to which all voltages of the measuring signals are related.

Gun See **electron gun.**

H

Helix A helically wound resistive coating on the inside of the conical part of the **CRT** to which a high voltage is applied to obtain **PDA.** [*Fig. 1.4*]

Hold-off period The period during which the **sweep generator** is inhibited from generating a new **sweep** after the previous one. This period starts at the end of each **sweep** coinciding with the start of the **flyback,** and ends ample time after the finish of the latter. [*Figs. 2.16 and 2.17*]

Horizontal channel All electronic circuits (**trigger circuit, sweep generator,** amplifier) providing the horizontal or X deflection on the **screen.** [*Fig. 1.13*]

Hum Objectionable line supply or mains-frequency components in an electrical signal path caused by improper operation of the power supply, direct induction into the signal leads by insufficient shielding, etc. [*Fig. 5.25*]

I

IEC specification A specification point which is described or stated according to one of the recommendations of the IEC (International Electrotechnical Commission). [*Chap. 7*]

Input coupling See **AC/DC input coupling.**

Input RC time In the ac-coupled input mode (see **AC/DC input coupling**), it is the product of the input resistance (usually 1 MΩ) and the coupling capacitor at the **Y input** of the **oscilloscope.**

Input sensitivity It is usually the minimum voltage at the input of the **vertical (horizontal) channel** needed for 1 **division** deflection of the **spot.** [*Chap. 7*]

Intensity A measure of the luminosity of the **spot** on the **screen.** [*Sec. 1.4*]

Internal triggering The **triggering** by which part of the **Y-input** signal is taken off internally for use as the **trigger source.** [*Sec. 2.6*]

Invert mode The ability to display the polarity-inverted **Y-input** signal. [*Sec. 2.4*]

J

Jitter The timing irregularities in a waveform (e.g., the period time) arising from fluctuations in line voltage, components, etc. Usually time jitter is expressed as a percent of the period time. [*Fig. 2.28*]

L

Line triggering **Triggering** at the line voltage frequency, obtained by deriving internally a **trigger signal** from the line power supply. [*Sec. 2.6*]

Loading effect The change in behavior of characteristics of a device under test due to the connection of the **probe** to the device. [*Sec. 6.1*]

Logic analyzer An electronic measuring instrument for the presentation on a **CRT** of digital information. [*Sec. 3.3*]

Logic trigger probe A multi-input (4, 8, or 16) **probe** which supplies a **trigger pulse** after detection of a digital logic word at the input such as preset by switches on the probe. [*Sec. 4.5*]

Loop gain (**1**) The total gain of an amplifier and feedback circuit; (**2**) in **sampling oscilloscopes** the gain in the signal path through the **sampling bridge,** amplifier, memory and feedback circuit. [*Fig. 3.18*]

Lossy coaxial cable A **coaxial cable** whose central conductor has been given a certain resistance. It is used as the cable for **passive probes.** [*Figs. 4.5 and 4.9*]

M

Magnifier See **time-base magnifier.**

Main time base (**1**) A base for the scale of time of the **sweep** generated by the **main-time-base circuit;** (**2**) Frequently used as an abbreviation for **main-time-base circuit.**

Main-time-base circuit See **time-base generator.** The addition "main" is only used to distinguish it from a second or **delayed-time-base circuit** in case the latter is built in also. [*Sec. 2.13*]

Mains triggering See **line triggering.** [*Sec. 2.6*]

Max write mode The mode in which the **writing speed** of the **variable-persistence storage CRT** is increased at the expense of contrast. [*Fig. 3.8*]

Measuring earth The common point for all signal voltages, also called **ground.** To be distinguished from **safety earth.**

Mesh The metal mesh electrode in a **CRT** located between the **deflection plates** and the **screen** to improve the **deflection sensitivity.** Flat meshes as well as curved (or domed) meshes are applied, the latter giving a greater increase in **deflection sensitivity.** [*Figs. 1.5 and 1.6*]

Mesh tube A **CRT** possessing a **mesh** electrode. [*Figs. 1.5 and 1.6*]

Mixed sweep The display in which after the **delay time** the **sweep speed** of the **main time base** is taken over by the one of the **delayed time base.** [*Sec. 2.16*]

Monoaccelerator tube A **CRT** not having **PDA.** [*Sec. 1.2*]

MTB Abbreviation for **main time base.**

Multichannel oscilloscope An **oscilloscope** able to handle more than two **Y-input** signals (usually 4 signals). [*Sec. 3.3*]

Multiplier oscilloscope An **oscilloscope** capable of displaying the instantaneous product of two input signals. [*Sec. 3.3*]

Multiply mode The way of displaying the instantaneous product of two signals. [*Sec. 3.3*]

N

Noise Any unwanted electrical signal in a signal path, such as rf interference or **hum** from the line supply. [*Fig. 3.26*]

O

Oscilloscope An electronic measuring instrument for the delineation of a wide range of the waveforms of electrical voltages by means of an **electron beam** in a **cathode-ray tube** (**CRT**) incorporated in the instrument.

Overshoot The maximum excursion of a signal **transition** (e.g., in **pulse voltages**) outside the range from the initial to the final mean levels, and usually expressed in percent of the range. For overshoot, the **transition** must be positive, or going from a low to a high signal level. This is in contrast to **undershoot.** [*Fig. 5.3*]

P

Parallax The apparent change in position of the displayed **waveform** on the **screen** against the external **graticule** when the viewing position of the observer is changed. [*Sec. 1.2*]

Passive probe A **probe** in which no active elements (transistors, amplifiers) are used. To be distinguished from **active probes.** [*Sec. 4.2*]

PDA See **postdeflection acceleration.**

Persistence In a **storage CRT,** it is the continued visibility when the exciting source (**beam**) has been removed. In a normal **CRT** it is usually called **phosphorescence.** [*Sec. 3.1*]

Phosphorescence The emission of light by the phosphor **screen** after excitation by the **electron beam.**

Photographic writing speed The **writing speed** registered by a photographic procedure under well-defined circumstances. [*Sec. 1.2*]

Plug-in oscilloscope An **oscilloscope** mechanically consisting of a mainframe to which various plug-in units may be added to vary the oscilloscope's facilities. To be distinguished from **compact oscilloscopes.** [*Sec. 3.3*]

Postdeflection acceleration The acceleration of the **electron beam** after the electrons have passed the **deflection plates.** [*Sec. 1.2*]

Preshoot In **pulse** voltages the excursion outside the initial mean level and in the opposite direction just before the start of a **transition,** usually expressed in percent of the transition's mean levels. [*Fig. 5.3*]

Probe A measuring electrode used to extract a fraction of the power from a circuit under test for visualization on an **oscilloscope.** [*Chap. 4*]

Probe adjustment The trimming of a **passive probe** by means of a trimming capacitor adjustable for optimum signal transfer from the **probe tip** to the **oscilloscope.** [*Fig. 4.8*]

Probe cable A **coaxial cable** connecting the front end of the **probe** to the **oscilloscope.**

Probe tip The top end of the **probe** which is actually connected to the circuit under test. [*Fig. 4.2*]

Protective insulation See **supplementary insulation.**

Pulse See **pulse voltage.**

Pulse response The response at the output of an electrical network (amplifier, attenuator) to an "ideal" **pulse voltage** applied to its input. Normally the response shows some kind of **distortion** of the "ideal" pulse. [*Figs. 5.2 and 5.3*]

Pulse space The time interval between two successive **pulses** for which the amplitudes exceed a specified proportion (usually 50%) of their respective maximum values. [*Fig. 5.4*]

Pulse voltage One **transient** or step in a voltage followed by a reverse step after a certain time interval. In the so-called "ideal" case the duration of both **transients** or steps is supposed to be zero. [*Figs. 5.1 and 5.2*]

Pulse width The time interval for which the amplitude of a **pulse voltage** exceeds a specified proportion (usually 50%) of its maximum value. [*Fig. 5.2*]

Pump generator An analog electronic circuit providing amounts of charge released by an independent input signal, usually **pulses.** [*Figs. 3.21 and 3.22*]

R

Ramp voltage See **sawtooth voltage.** [*Sec. 2.9*]

Random sampling **Samples** taken at points selected at random throughout the signal **waveform.** [*Sec. 3.2*]

Real-time oscilloscope See **oscilloscope;** the addition "real time" is meant to distinguish it from the **sampling oscilloscope.**

Register   A digital memory element. [*Sec. 3.3*]

Ringing   A damped oscillation occurring after a **transition** in the signal, e.g., in **pulse voltages.** [*Fig. 4.7*]

Rise time   (**1**) The time for a **transient** to rise from 10 to 90% of the maximum amplitude [*Fig. 5.2*] (**2**) In **oscilloscopes,** stating the **pulse response** of the **vertical channel.** The relation to the **bandwidth** (-3 dB) can be approximated by: bandwidth (Hz) × rise time (seconds) = 0.35. [*Sec. 5.3*]

Rouding   The gradual changeover in **pulse signals** from the **transition** to the final value. [*Fig. 5.2*]

S

Safety earth   A ground terminal connected to the protective earth or ground according to the safety requirements for systems or instruments. To be distinguished from **measuring earth.**

Sag   See **droop.**

Sample   In **sampling oscilloscopes** it is the instantaneous value of the **Y-input** voltage, as such measured during a minute interval of time (100–200 ps). [*Sec. 3.2*]

Sampling   Taking a specimen as a part to illustrate the whole. See also **sampling oscilloscope.**

Sampling bridge   A particular circuit comprising a **sampling gate.** [*Fig. 3.18*]

Sampling gate   In a **sampling oscilloscope** it is a **gate** performing the **sampling** process, and usually comprising a diode-resistor network. [*Sec. 3.2*]

Sampling oscilloscope   An **oscilloscope** measuring the amplitudes of the vertical or **Y-input** signals by frequently taking samples over minute intervals of time. The instantaneous values of the amplitude are stored in a memory for display on the **screen.** [*Sec. 3.2*]

Sampling pulse   A **pulse** (**spike**) enabling the **sampling gate.** [*Sec. 3.2 and Fig. 3.21*]

Sawtooth voltage   A ramp signal linearly increasing with time which, after having reached its maximum level, drops back to its zero level. The ramp is used to obtain a linear time scale at the **oscilloscope screen** in the horizontal, or X, direction. [*Sec. 2.9 and Fig. 1.11*]

Schmitt trigger   An electronic circuit providing an output **pulse** signal of which the **pulse width** is determined by the time that any input voltage exceeds a certain level. [*Sec. 6.2*]

Screen   The flat front end of the **CRT** onto which the energy of the **beam** of electrons is transferred into light by the **phosphorescence** of the phosphor deposited on its inside surface. [*Fig. 1.2*]

Secondary emission The emission of electrons from a surface (for example, the **storage layer** in a **storage CRT**) by the bombardment of the surface by high-energy electrons from another source. [*Sec. 3.1*]

Segmented deflection plates **Deflection plates** which are divided into smaller plates which, together with external components, coils, etc., connected to them, constitute a **delay line.** Such a system is only used for the vertical **deflection plates** and results in a higher **bandwidth** of the **CRT**. [*Fig. 1.3B*]

Sensitivity See **input sensitivity.**

Sequential sampling The taking of samples sequentially at adjacent points throughout the signal **waveform.** [*Sec. 3.2*]

Shift range The range that the **spot** or trace can be moved from the central horizontal and/or vertical **graticule** line, and specified in a number of **divisions.**

Single-beam CRT See **single-gun CRT.**

Single-gun CRT A **CRT** with one **electron gun.** [*Fig. 1.2*]

Single-trace oscilloscope An **oscilloscope** which allows the display of only one signal.

Single-sweep mode The trigger mode in which only one single **sweep** is allowed, after the **sweep generator** has been set first. [*Sec. 2.10*]

Spike A sharp, time-isolated, spike-shaped **pulse,** often used for **trigger** purposes.

Split-beam CRT A **single-gun CRT** in which two writing beams are obtained by splitting the **beam.** [*Fig. 2.3*]

Split-beam oscilloscope An **oscilloscope** possessing a **split-beam CRT.**

Spot The focused point of the **electron beam** on the **screen** of a **CRT.**

Square-wave signal A **pulse signal** with equidistant time intervals between the up and down **transients,** which are in themselves very short relative to the time intervals. [*Fig. 7.4*]

Storage CRT A **CRT** that can retain a display for a long time (minutes, hours) or until it is deliberately **erased.** [*Sec. 3.1*]

Storage layer The layer in a **storage tube** retaining the pattern written on it by the **electron beam.** [*Figs. 3.2 and 3.3*]

Storage mesh The mesh inside the **variable-persistence storage CRT** carrying the **storage layer.** [*Figs. 3.2 and 3.3*]

Storage oscilloscope An **oscilloscope** with a **storage CRT.** [*Sec. 3.1*]

Storage tube See **storage CRT.**

Supplementary (protective) insulation Independent insulation provided in addition to, and at least of the same electrical strength as, the **functional insulation,**

to ensure protection against electric shock in the event of failure of the **functional insulation.**

Sweep The uniform motion of the **spot** across the **screen** in horizontal, or X, direction. [*Sec. 1.3*]

Sweep generator The electronic circuit producing the **sweep voltage,** is also called the **time-base generator.** [*Figs. 1.11 and 2.16*]

Sweep speed The speed of the **sweep** expressed in **divisions** per (fraction of) second. It is the inverse of the **time coefficient.**

Sweep voltage The **sawtooth voltage** generated in an **oscilloscope** and used as horizontal, or X, **deflection voltage** to obtain a linear time scale on the **screen.**

T

Terminated HF probe An attenuating ($10\times$ or $100\times$) high-frequency **probe** with relatively low input impedance (500 Ω or 5 kΩ). [*Fig. 4.9*]

Termination See **cable termination.**

Tilt See **droop.**

Time coefficient The time scale of the **sweep** expressed in (fractions of) seconds per **division.** It is the inverse of **sweep speed.**

Time-domain reflectometry Observing on an **oscilloscope** the response of an "ideal" **pulse** at the input of a transmission line. [*Sec. 6.1*]

Timebase (**1**) Base for the scale of time of the **sweep.** (**2**) Frequently used as an abbreviation for **time-base circuit.**

Time-base generator The electronic circuit producing the **sweep** signal to obtain a (calibrated) time scale on the **screen.** [*Fig. 2.16*]

Time-base magnifier The circuit contained in the horizontal output amplifier providing faster **sweep speeds** (often 5 or 10 times faster). [*Sec. 2.12*]

Top triggering The **trigger mode** by which the **trigger level** is derived internally from the **trigger signal** and fixed near to the peak value. [*Sec. 2.8*]

Transfer storage CRT A **variable-persistence storage CRT** with two **storage meshes** of which the first (as seen from the **flood guns**) is optimized for fast storage and the second is optimized for a long storage time. In a **single-sweep** routine the pattern is written by the **electron beam** on the first mesh. At the end of the **sweep** it is transferred to the second mesh by means of applied voltages. [*Fig. 3.10*]

Transient A rapid change in a **waveform.**

Transition The rapid change of the signal from one level to another. See also **transient.** [*Sec. 2.5*]

Trigger See **trigger pulse.**

Trigger circuit   A circuit producing **pulses** at the output each time the input signal passes some selected level. The trigger output **pulses** activate the **sweep generator.** [*Figs. 1.13 and 2.10*]

Trigger coupling   The means by which a part of the **trigger circuit** provides frequency filtering of the **trigger signal.** [*Figs. 2.10 and 2.11*]

Trigger level   The selected voltage level an input signal must pass to produce **trigger pulses** at the output of a **trigger circuit.** [*Figs. 2.10 and 2.13*]

Trigger mode   The way in which the desired **triggering** is obtained (**auto triggering, single sweep,** etc.).

Trigger pick-off   The point in the Y channel where the **trigger signal** is taken off and fed to the **trigger source** circuit. [*Fig. 2.9*]

Trigger pulse   An electrical signal used for **triggering,** such as at the output of a **trigger circuit.** [*Fig. 2.13*]

Trigger sensitivity   The minimum signal amplitude required for proper **triggering** expressed in **divisions** in the case of **internal triggering,** or volts in the case of **external triggering.** [*Sec. 2.8*]

Trigger signal   The signal from which the **trigger pulse** is derived.

Trigger slope   The upward (positive) or downward (negative) slope of the **trigger signal** at which the **sweep** is started by **triggering.** [*Figs. 2.10 and 2.13*]

Trigger source   The source from which the signal is used as the **trigger signal.** [*Sec. 2.6*]

Trigger take-off   See **trigger pick-off.** [*Fig. 2.9*]

Triggering   The initiation of the **sweep** by applying to the **sweep generator,** a **trigger pulse** which is derived from, or possesses a time relation with, the signal to be measured (**Y-input** signal). [*Sec. 1.3*]

TTL triggering   The **trigger mode** in which the **trigger level** control is adapted to the two logical levels for TTL input circuits. Logical zero is between 0 and 0.8 V and logical one is between 2.0 and 5.0 V. [*Figs. 3.45 and 3.46*]

TV Triggering   The **triggering** by which television frame or line synchronization pulses are used to derive **trigger pulses** internally. [*Sec. 3.3*]

U

Unblanking   This permits the **electron beam** in a **CRT** to pass through the **gun** towards the **screen.** This is controlled by a voltage applied between the **cathode** and the **Wehnelt cylinder.**

Unblanking pulse   A **pulse**-shaped signal applied to the **CRT** for **unblanking.** [*Fig. 2.16*]

Undershoot   As **overshoot** but for negative-going **transitions.** [*Fig. 5.3*]

V

Variable persistence The **persistence** of which the time of continued visibility after exciting can be varied. [*Sec. 3.1*]

Vertical channel All the electronic circuitry including **attenuator** and amplifiers from the **Y-input** bus as far as the vertical, or *Y* deflection plates. [*Fig. 1.13*]

Vertical input The input bus of the **Y**, or **vertical, channel.**

Voltage probe A **probe** designed to sense voltages. [*Secs. 4.2 and 4.3*]

W

Waveform In oscilloscopy it is the magnitude (or value) versus time relationship of an electrical signal.

Wehnelt cylinder The part of the **electron gun** by means of which the **intensity** of the **beam** is controlled by supplying to it a voltage with respect to the **cathode.** [*Fig. 1.2*]

Writing speed The maximum speed of a single **sweep** that can be observed on the screen. [*Figs. 1.7 and 1.8*]

Writing system In a **storage CRT** the part that has to be distinguished from the **flood system** and which is identical to the same part in a normal **CRT** consisting of the **electron gun** and the **deflection plates.** [*Fig. 3.2*]

X

X channel See **horizontal channel.**

Y

Y channel See **vertical channel.**

Y input The input bus of the **Y,** or **vertical, channel.**

Z

Z modulation The modulation of the **brightness** by means of a modulating voltage applied between the **cathode** and the **Wehnelt cylinder.**

APPENDIX B
Tables of Notations,
Symbols, and Units

Decimal multiples and submultiples of International System (SI) units are formed by means of the prefixes given in the following table:

Multiples	Submultiples
10^{12} = tera = T	10^{-1} = deci = d
10^9 = giga = G	10^{-2} = centi = c
10^6 = mega = M	10^{-3} = milli = m
10^3 = kilo = k	10^{-6} = micro = μ
10^2 = hecto = h	10^{-9} = nano = n
10 = deca = da	10^{-12} = pico = p
	10^{-15} = femto = f
	10^{-18} = atto = a

The period placed on the line is recommended as the decimal sign. The center dot is used as the multiplication sign with compound units.

ADVISED NOTATIONS

	Column 1	Column 2A	Column 2B
Instantaneous value	x	X	x
Root-mean-square value of a periodic quantity	X	$\bar{X}$ X_{rms}	$\bar{x}$ x_{rms}
Peak value	$\hat{x},\hat{X}$ x_m,X_m	$\hat{X}$ X_m	$\hat{x}$ x_m
Average value	$\bar{x},\bar{X}$ x_{av},X_{av}	$\bar{X}$ X_{av}	$\bar{x}$ x_{av}

The minimum value of a pulsating quantity may be denoted by $\check{x}$, $\check{X}$ or x_{min}, X_{min} so that the peak-to-valley value is $(\hat{x} - \check{x})$ or $(\hat{X} - \check{X})$ and $(x_m - x_{min})$, or $(X_m - X_{min})$.

Quantities which vary with time may be indicated as follows:

• If capital and lowercase letters are appropriate column 1 applies.

• If only capital letters or only lowercase letter are appropriate, column 2A or 2B applies.

The International System of units (SI) is founded on the following base units:

Quantity	Base unit	Symbol
Length	meter	m
Mass	kilogram	kg
Time	second	s
Electric current	ampere	A
Thermodynamic temp.	kelvin	K
Amount of substance	mole	mol
Luminous intensity	candela	cd

THE INTERNATIONAL SYSTEM (SI) OF UNITS FOR ELECTRICITY

| Quantity | | SI unit | | Conversions | Base units |
Name	Symbol	Name	Unit		(m, kg, s, A)
Electric current	I	ampere	A		A
Electric current density	J, (S)	ampere per square meter	A/m²		$m^{-2} \cdot A$
Electric charge, quantity of electricity	Q	coulomb	C	$1\,C = 1\,A \cdot s$	$s \cdot A$
Electric potential	V, φ	volt	V	$1\,V = 1\,W/A$ Link to base units: $1\,V$ = energy per unity of charge $= 1\,J/C = 1\,N \cdot m/C$ $= 1\,kg \cdot m^2/(A \cdot s^3)$	$m^2 \cdot kg \cdot s^{-3} \cdot A^{-1}$
Electrical potential difference, electric tension (voltage)	U, (V)				
Electric source voltage, electromotive force	E				
Power*	P	watt	W	$1\,W = 1\,V \cdot A = 1\,J/s$	$m^2 \cdot kg \cdot s^{-3}$
Energy	W	joule	J	$1\,J = 1\,W \cdot s = 1\,N \cdot m$	$m^2 \cdot kg \cdot s^{-2}$
Impedance	Z				
Resistance	R	ohm	Ω	$1\,\Omega = 1\,V/A$	$m^2 \cdot kg \cdot s^{-3} \cdot A^{-2}$
Reactance	X				

THE INTERNATIONAL SYSTEM (SI) OF UNITS FOR ELECTRICITY (continued)

Quantity		SI unit		Conversions	Base units (m, kg, s, A)
Name	Symbol	Name	Unit		
Admittance	Y			$1\ S = 1\ A/V = 1/\Omega$	$m^{-2} \cdot kg^{-1} \cdot s^3 \cdot A^2$
Conductance	G	siemen	S	$Y = 1/Z$	
Susceptance	B			$G = 1/R \qquad B = 1/X$	
Specific resistance, resistivity	ρ	ohm-meter	$\Omega \cdot m$		$m^3 \cdot kg \cdot s^{-3} \cdot A^{-2}$
Specific conductance, conductivity	γ, σ	siemens per meter	S/m	$\gamma = 1/\rho$	$m^{-3} \cdot kg^{-1} \cdot s^3 \cdot A^2$
Electric flux ($= \int D_n dS$)	Ψ	coulomb	C		$s \cdot A$
Electric field strength	E	volt per meter	V/m	$1\ V/m = 1\ N/C$	$m \cdot kg \cdot s^{-3} \cdot A^{-1}$
Dielectric displacement	D	coulomb per square meter	C/m^2		$m^{-2} \cdot s \cdot A$
Electric polarization	P, (D)			$P = D - \varepsilon_0 E$	
Electric dipole moment	p, P_e	coulomb-meter	$C \cdot m$		$m \cdot s \cdot A$
Capacitance	C	farad	F	$1\ F = 1\ C/V$ $C = Q/U$	$m^{-2} \cdot kg^{-1} \cdot s^4 \cdot A^2$

Quantity	Symbol	Unit		Relation	Base units
Permittivity, dielectric constant	ε	farad per meter	F/m	$\varepsilon = D/E$	$m^{-3} \cdot kg^{-1} \cdot s^4 \cdot A^2$
Permittivity of vacuum, electric constant	ε_0	farad per meter	F/m	$\varepsilon_0 = 10^{-9}/(36 \cdot \pi)F/m$	$m^{-3} \cdot kg^{-1} \cdot s^4 \cdot A^2$
Relative permittivity	ε_r	(dimensionless)	—	$\varepsilon_r = \varepsilon/\varepsilon_0$	—
Relative electric susceptibility	χ, χ_e	(dimensionless)	—	$\chi = \varepsilon_r - 1$	—
Magnetic flux $(= \int B_n dS)$	Φ	weber	Wb	$1\ Wb = 1\ V \cdot s$	$m^2 \cdot kg \cdot s^{-2} \cdot A$
Magnetic field strength	H	ampere per meter	A/m	$1\ A/m = 1\ N/Wb$	$m^{-1} \cdot A$
Magnetic induction	B	weber per square meter (tesla)	Wb/m² (T)		$kg \cdot s^{-2} \cdot A^{-1}$
Magnetic polarization	J			$J = B - \mu_0 H$	$kg \cdot s^{-2} \cdot A^{-1}$
Magnetic dipole moment	j	weber-meter	Wb · m		$m^3 \cdot kg \cdot s^{-2} \cdot A^{-1}$
Self-inductance	L	henry	H	$1\ H = 1\ V \cdot s/A = 1\ Wb/A$	$m^2 \cdot kg \cdot s^{-2} \cdot A^{-1}$
Mutual inductance	M, L_{12}	henry	H	$1\ H = 1\ V \cdot s/A = 1\ Wb/A$	$m^2 \cdot kg \cdot s^{-2} \cdot A^{-2}$

THE INTERNATIONAL SYSTEM (SI) OF UNITS FOR ELECTRICITY (continued)

| Quantity | SI unit | | | Base units |
Name	Symbol	Name	Unit	Conversions	(m, kg, s, A)
Permeability magnetic induction constant	μ	henry per meter	H/m	$\mu = B/H$	$m \cdot kg \cdot s^{-2} \cdot A^{-2}$
Permeability of vacuum, magnetic induction constant	μ_0			$\mu_0 = 4\pi \cdot 10^{-7} H/m$	
Relative permeability	μ_r	(dimensionless)	—	$\mu_r = \mu/\mu_0$	—
Relative magnetic permeability	x_r	(dimensionless)	—	$x_r = \mu_r - 1$	—
Phase displacement	φ	radian	rad		—
Frequency	f, ν	hertz	Hz	$1\ Hz = 1/s$	s^{-1}
Angular frequency, angular velocity	ω	radian per second	rad/s	$\omega = 2\pi \cdot f$	s^{-1}

* In electric power technology, active power (symbol P) is expressed in the unit watt (W); apparent power (symbol S or P_s) in volt-ampere (V · A) and reactive (positive or negative) power (symbol Q or P_q) in var (var).

INDEX